The History of Doctor Johann Faustus

H. G. HAILE is associate professor of German and chairman of the Department of Germanic Languages and Literature at the University of Illinois. He also is the author of *Das Faustbuch nach der Wolfenbüttler Handschrift*.

University of Illinois Press, Urbana, 1965

The
History
of
Doctor Johann Faustus

Recovered from the German by **H. G. Haile**

to
Mary Elizabeth

Contents

INTRODUCTION

HISTORIA & TALE
OF DOCTOR JOHANNES FAUSTUS

BIBLIOGRAPHICAL NOTE

Introduction

GEORG FAUSTUS, THE DEVIL'S BROTHER-IN-LAW

Bamberg is an ancient city in central Germany, probably best known by the four tall towers of its fine medieval cathedral, where some of our most treasured pieces of Gothic sculpture are preserved. That cathedral was just about five hundred years old when, in early February of the year 1520, the Bishop's secretary — a fellow with the wonderfully ordinary name of Hans Müller — wrote the following entry into his ledgers under the heading *Miscellaneous*:

> 10 Gulden, paid in hand to Doctor Faustus, phil., as an honorarium for a nativity, or horoscope, for the Bishop. — The Sunday after Saint Scholastica's Day. By order of the Bishop.

Mutianus Rufus in the town of Gotha — just north of the Thuringian Forest from Bamberg — was probably also referring to this astrologer when in 1513 he warned a friend in nearby Erfurt that Georg Faustus, "a mere braggart and fool," was passing through their region.

Still earlier, isolated reports may have to do with the same man, but we cannot be sure. From the year 1507, for example, there survives a long letter from an abbot in Würzburg to a professor in Heidelberg about one Georg Sabellicus, a practitioner of black magic who sometimes called himself Faustus junior. Is this our Georg Faustus? Who, then, would Faustus senior have been? A sorcerer from the previous century? There were many men in the late Middle Ages who claimed occult powers, as well as many others who enjoyed — or suffered from — the reputation. It is probably not possible to make a clear distinction between the historical Faust and forerunners of the Faust figure, which certainly possesses kindred spirits almost as old as humanity — the Witch of Endor in the Book of Samuel was practicing an already ancient art. One popular legend which survived into the fifteenth and sixteenth centuries was that of Theophilus, a pious cleric who was led by circumstance into a pact with the devil, but was redeemed by the Virgin. Similar pacts were frequently invented as a popular explanation for accomplishments of famous scholars. Doctor Faustus, who deliberately associated himself with this tradition, became the peculiarly German necromancer and devil's thane to rise up right between the Middle Ages and Modern Times, in a somehow peculiarly German century.

The printing press, earlier attributed to magic, was now coming into general use. In the same year that Hans Müller made his ledger entry, a young professor from the newly founded University of Wittemberg was preparing the all-time best seller for Gutenberg's invention, a New Testament in the vernacular. Doctor Luther, hidden away by his friends at the fortress Wartburg, created for his Bible a language so forthright and easily understood throughout Central Europe that it quickly took on more than religious significance — just as did the Protestant Reformation in which the German Bible was only one significant event. The religious revival, Protestant and Catholic, was in turn part of a greater general movement in which worldly men were active, too, transforming political and economic systems over the whole continent.

This was the day not only of Luther with his brutal integrity, but also of the gentle, sophisticated Erasmus. It was a superstitious time when Doctor Faustus duped learned men, and it was the hard, common-sense age of the business man. The Nuremberg cobbler Hans Sachs was writing realistic comedies, and his fellow citizen Albrecht Dürer was scrutinizing the animate and inanimate world with a hitherto unheard-of precision. Ancient occult sciences, inherited from Egypt and the Near East, were still flourishing throughout Europe. Astrology and alchemy, nurtured by the Middle Ages, were becoming primitive astronomy and chemistry, for this was also the day of Copernicus in Prussia and of Paracelsus in Switzerland. The University of Cracow offered a degree in Black Magic.

The feudal nobility felt itself economically undermined by a newly wealthy, usually Protestant townsfolk, and oppressed at the same time by the waxing power of petty princes. The early sixteenth century saw many of the old lords become robber barons, poised at their fortresses atop craggy heights and at river bends, ready to descend upon the fat, successful merchants whenever these dared venture outside their walled towns. The towns themselves, embryos of our modern democracy, are another development of the age. Names of the men who stormed their walls in vain, representatives of a dying class and a bygone era, are not entirely forgotten: Götz von Berlichingen With the Iron Hand, a leader in the Peasants' Revolts, who doggedly set down his concepts of freedom and rugged individualism in an autobiography which still stirs our sympathies; or Franz von Sickingen, the most powerful of the renegades and, incidentally, a personal friend of the astrologer who called himself Doctor Faustus. But it is undoubtedly another of Sickingen's friends, Ulrich von Hutten, a knight of old with peculiarly modern political ideals, a devoted Humanist and at the same time a militant Protestant, an eloquent Latinist as well as a rabble-rouser in fresh, rough German rhymes, who is most typical of the early sixteenth century, for it was an age of great contrasts, looking backward toward the Middle Ages and forward toward modern times.

New national states were emerging in the Old World, and a New World was being discovered abroad. From it came corn, potatoes, tomatoes, tobacco and syphilis, the disease which killed Ulrich von Hutten. A cousin of his, Philip von Hutten, who died exploring America, wrote a letter from Coro, Venezuela, in January of 1540, which said, in part: "We here in Venezola are not the only ones who have suffered. All the aforementioned fleets that set out from Sevilla before and after us perished within three month's time. Thus I have to confess that the philosopher Faust was just about right, because we have had a very bad year."

Secretary Hans Müller's record of payment and Philip von Hutten's letter from "Venezola" are typical of many other surviving documents which attest to the existence of an astrologer named Faust who was wandering around Germany in those years (1520-1540). We have various letters and diaries in which well-known contemporaries — including Martin Luther and Philip Melanchthon — record their personal knowledge of his comings and goings. Two city councils took actions pertaining to him and duly recorded their decisions. This is how we know that Faust was banished from Ingolstadt in June of 1528, and that he was denied entry into Nuremberg in May of 1532. The man's first name was probably Georg, and he assumed titles as fitted the specific occasion: philosopher, demigod, the Devil's brother-in-law. He seems to have been a very clever rascal, well versed in alchemistical tricks and in other matters, too — the magic lantern, for example, with which he could conjure up heroes out of the past. He was certainly a shameless braggart and a mountebank — a charlatan in a gullible age.

From Hans Müller and Philip von Hutten we know that both the clergy and the nobility respected his art. From other letters we discover that he even commanded the somewhat dubious respect of learned men, although they preferred openly to

4

renounce him. In all fairness, we ought to admit that any practitioner before the public is something of an empiric, and that the physic of old — including this Georg Faust — may well have believed in his own gifts much as does the modern physician or physicist. His powers may even to some extent have been genuine. But it is also clear that Georg Faust was a man of known moral laxity, given to drink and to sexual perversions — undoubtedly to a risky personal existence in general — so that the vague reports of his spectacular, violent death around 1540 are entirely credible. People said at the time that the Devil had fetched him away.

JOHANN FAUSTUS

One of the men who seems to have known Georg Faust well is Luther's Humanist friend and helper, the most respected leader in Protestantism after Luther's death, Philip Melanchthon. Melanchthon had gone to Heidelberg to enroll as a student at the university there in 1509. It so happened that a young man named Johann Faust graduated in that very year at the head of his class, something which must have impressed the young Philip Melanchthon. Since both *Johann* and *Faust* were widespread names in Germany, this 1509 Heidelberg valedictorian probably has no further connection with the famous astrologer Georg Faust — but the coincidence of names seems to have become an important connection. Years later, when speaking to his students of the astrologer who was born not far from his own home town, Professor Melanchthon, perhaps because of a lapse of memory, called the astrologer Johann Faust. One of his students set down the name in careful notes which were later published and, because of Melanchthon's prominence, widely read.

Particularly after the death of Georg Faust around 1540, the number of surviving references to Johann Faust increases. The further separated in time a source may be from the actual historical deeds of Georg Faust, just that much more extensively and richly are the character and exploits of Johann Faust depicted. As early as 1548, a Swiss clergyman is able to tell how Faust sent a devil to haunt a monastery where one of the brothers had refused him the best wines in the cellar. The same clergyman goes on to relate how Faust's devil, who accompanied him in the form of a dog or a horse, would bring exotic birds to Faust's table. At last Satan strangled Faust and took him away to Hell.

It seems likely that the first collection of Faust tales was made by Wolf Wambach in the university town of Erfurt. This town chronicler must have been a man of imagination, for in his tales Faust first takes on the characteristic personality which made him so attractive to poets of subsequent ages. It is the character of a brilliant heretic among stuffy academicians, of a researcher into forbidden knowledge feared by the professors. Wambach's Faust, when lecturing on Homer at the University of Erfurt, conjures up some heroes and other figures from the Trojan War. Their aspect is so frightening —Cyclops appears with Greeks dangling from his teeth — that the audience runs away. When some professors express mild regrets that so many classics have been lost, Faust volunteers to recover all the works of Plautus and Terence; but the professors of theology will not allow it, insisting that the Devil could well slip in all sorts of objectionable and improper passages. It is understood that this Faust is in league with infernal powers. We see him in one tale summon his devils, asking them one by one how fast they travel, but rejecting all until he finds one as quick as the thoughts of men. In a last tale, a Franciscan monk tries to convert Faust and promises to say many masses in his behalf. "Here a mass, there a mass," growls Faust, "my pledge binds me too hard." He has given the Devil his word and is too proud to go back on it.

We have Wambach's tales only at second hand, for the chronicle into which he entered them is lost. Our oldest surviving collection of Faust tales is a group of four put together by a citizen of Nuremberg, Christoph Rosshirt, sometime in the 1570's. Here Faust uses his Black Arts for the good life only.

6

He serves his guests fine food and drink stolen by his devils from a great ball being held by the King of England, and afterward he transports his whole party in an instant to the English Court. He borrows money from a Jew, refuses to pay him back, and when the Jew calls for payment pretends to be in a sound sleep. The Jew attempts to wake Faust by pulling on his leg, whereupon the leg comes flying out of Faust's body and the Jew flees lest he be charged with murder. From bundles of straw, Faust charms a herd of fine fat swine which he sells cheap, warning the buyer not to drive them into water. When these instructions are disregarded, the swine change back into bundles of straw and go floating away. At an inn, noisy peasants disturb Faust, who casts a spell on them so that they cannot open their mouths. Rosshirt's last tale tells how the sorcerer is found in his bed, murdered by the Devil.

Such stories must be typical of what was being told about Faust all over South and Central Germany in the 1560's and 1570's — or about a generation after his death — for other writers of the period tell similar and often identical ones. Rosshirt's stories are not new ones at all, but merely rehashings of ancient tricks which magicians and other rascals had been playing on the people for centuries. Now all these tales begin to be connected with Faust, so that his figure becomes a collage of many personalities, some of them historical and some of them legendary. All the old tricks are now played anew by that braggart who became a legend in his own lifetime and who had died within the memory of a generation which now began to identify countless time-worn folk motifs with the name of Doctor Faustus.

Georg Faust cast a long shadow across the sixteenth century. No part of that shadow is identical with the man who cast it. The historical Georg and the folk Johann are two distinct Fausts.

THE FAUST BOOK

Then, perhaps before 1580, a third Faust was born, for someone wrote a little novel whose hero belongs neither to fact nor to

7

folklore. The forgotten novelist did not know, or care, to distinguish between the two. He sought only to produce a piece of light entertainment — exciting in that it dealt with abominations, sophisticated in that the blasphemous hero was presented not entirely unsympathetically, serious only to the extent that it did justify itself by demonstrating that Faust went to Hell for the same reasons that all good Catholics were going there: for the abominable arrogance, namely, of seeking salvation on his own hook, for the sin of doubting the exclusive sufficiency of God's Grace, for the vain presumption that he might try to *deserve* redemption, for his utmost pride that his own depravity could exceed the forgiving power of Divine Grace (this a blow delivered in passing at deviationist Protestant brethren).

At the very outset, the unknown author is eager to establish a hard-core Protestant position as the central theme of his novel. Thus the brief account of Faust's youth and schooling really amounts to a statement of his inborn wickedness. The anti-Catholic groundplan begins to be developed during Faust's negotiations and subsequent pact with his devil Mephostophiles, and it becomes explicit during his first researches at the end of Part One: a series of disputations in which Mephosto is compelled to provide Faust with occult and para-theological information on the devils, Hell and the Grace of God.

Certain related questions permit a more direct inquiry, so that Faust in Part Two makes a personal tour of Hell; he is carried up into the sky to examine the heavenly bodies at close range; at last he journeys around through the world, visiting the seat of Catholicism and the seat of Islam, to make ribald sport of both Pope and Sultan. He returns to Germany and shares his findings with scholarly friends. There is his delightful letter to a *Medicus* in Leipzig about his "Ascension into Heaven." He discourses with a learned Doctor from Halberstadt on comets, falling stars and the devils that reside beneath Heaven.

Part Three of the Faust Book consists of a series of cleverly formulated tales in which Faust's adventures are recounted.

They do not correspond with the recorded activities of the historical Faust — but they are related to folk literature. Each adventure combines folk motifs in an artful way and usually has a clever ending which adapts the material specifically for Faust and for the light entertainment of the Faust Book. Since the relationship between these tales and folklore is of particular help in understanding the further fortunes of the Faust Book, we ought to have a closer look at some of them.

An abbot of the monastery at Sponheim (near Kreuznach) in the early 1500's was a very famous alchemist, and some thought he was a sorcerer with a familiar spirit. The story went that he came to Emperor Maximilian and conjured up certain long dead historical personages for him. Luther told about it, and so did Hans Sachs. Maximilian had the reputation of indulging from time to time in magic himself, and in another old tale is supposed to have charmed horse's hooves onto one of his guests at table. The guest then asked imperial permission to perform a little trick of his own. Hardly was permission granted before a great noise arose outside the dining hall. When Emperor Max leaned out the window to see what could be the matter, his guest charmed a set of antlers onto the Emperor's head so that he could not draw it in again, but had to admit himself bested. Luther told this tale, too.

Now the Faust of the Faust Book (in Chapter 23) is invited to court by noblemen whom he has aided with prophecies and cured from diseases. Emperor Charles V sees him here, asks and is told who he is, and bids him come into his privy chamber. Here he tells Faust how he regrets that he can never rise to the eminence and power of an Alexander of old, whose ancient glory is now divided into many kingdoms. Charles asks if Faust could do him the kindness of letting him see Alexander as he looked in life. Faust explains that it is of course impossible to raise the dead. The spirits, however, being old and experienced and having lived in the time of Alexander, can indeed take on Alexander's outer appearance — if the Emperor will but promise to remain silent during the performance. Charles is willing, so that both Alexander and his consort appear, one after the other, each bowing low before the Emperor of Christendom. Now Charles has heard that the lady had a wart on her back side. In order to test the veracity of the spirits, he goes and lifts the skirt of the phantom, beholds the wart in its proper place, and is satisfied.

In the next chapter, Faust, still at the Imperial Court, notices a nobleman taking a noonday nap with his head hanging out a window and, for the fun of it, charms a set of hart's antlers onto the poor nobleman, thus humiliating him before his peers.

Such adventures are not arranged in the Faust Book at random, but with a certain organizational intent. In the last part of the novel, the same nobleman turns up again. He is riding with his men near a wood where Faust is taking a stroll. Remembering the insult he suffered at court, he orders a charge on Faust. Suddenly a whole army of phantom soldiers appears and takes the nobleman prisoner. Faust deprives him and his men of their steeds and sends them riding home on charmed horses — which disappear when ridden through water.

Thus the Faust-Book author concludes his tale with the old folk motif of the straw animals, which Christoph Rosshirt first connected with Faust. Before Rosshirt, it had been told about horses, swine, or cattle charmed into existence and sold by this or that sorcerer. The cheated buyer usually returned to find the sorcerer asleep and, as with Rosshirt, the rascal's leg, when tugged upon, came flying off in the poor buyer's hands.

The author of the Faust Book adapts this latter motif in his own way, too. In Chapter 26, Faust has spent all his money and must ask his spirit for more. Mephosto, in a paternal tone, points out that he has taught his protégé enough by now to enable him to earn his own keep. When new financial needs arise, Faust follows Mephosto's advice. He borrows money from a Jew, refuses to repay it when the loan comes due, but offers instead surety in the form of some part of his body. Shylock willingly

10

saws off one of Faust's legs, realizing only later that he has obtained a pretty worthless chattel. After he has thrown it away, he can no longer enforce his usurious contract.

This is the sort of adventure the Faust Book contains: stories reminiscent indeed of folk tale, but distinguished by an author's ability to combine various motifs and to adapt them to his hero. The chapters are organized in such a way as to yield transitions from one to the other and into the final section of the novel. The last adventure in Part Three tells about the attempt of a well-meaning, pious old neighbor to convert Faust. It leads to a second blood pact in which Faust must sign away his soul anew (the second pact, according to some devil lore, is the really binding one).

The gloomy Fourth Part reveals Faust using his arts to give questionable help to others, but taking no personal satisfaction from them. He makes final arrangements for his servant. The long and beautifully written last chapter restates the themes of Part One and gives account of Faust's death and damnation.

THE FAUST BOOK AT THE HANDS OF THE SCRIBES

The novel we have been discussing is, of course, the Faust Book as you will read it here. It is not, however, any book which we really have. This earliest, lost Faust Book was in manuscript. The manuscript was copied, and in copying it was augmented. Almost everyone in Germany in the latter half of the sixteenth century was something of a Faust authority: that is, the man whose spectacular death had occurred only a few years back was well known, and of course there were many who could tell tales — authentic or otherwise — about Doctor Faustus. The unknown copyist of the Faust manuscript was, as might be expected, especially well informed on his topic. Time and again the material he had before him called to mind another tale he knew. And well it might. The original author had, after all, drawn on well-known fact and popular folklore when he formed his novel.

Let us take as an example the story of the nobleman who sought to avenge himself on Faust. It was placed toward the end of the novel as a rounding-out of the adventures, for they had begun at the Imperial Court where Faust had incurred this nobleman's wrath in the first place. But right at the beginning of Part Three the copyist now saw fit to enter his own little tale about the nobleman's attempted revenge. Fortunately, when he came to the end of Part Three, the copyist reproduced the author's tale, too, but as a result we now have the same story told twice in the Faust Book.

The author had worked the folk motif of the charmed animals and straw bundles into his version to give the tale its clever ending. Elsewhere, the copyist retold that story, too, in a couple of its most familiar forms. Then he went on to use it still another time in order to tell the old horsedealer swindle from Christoph Rosshirt; the Shylock story (Chapter 26) seems to have reminded him of it. And so it goes throughout Part Three. Again and again the copyist felt constrained to add some good Faust story which he thought the author had neglected.

The Faust Book contains more than adventures, of course. It touches upon fundamental points of theology, and it discusses what in that day passed for science. The copyist, who did not feel he was dealing with fiction at all, but rather with a factual report on a vital topic, thought he was obliged to make the work as complete and as reliable as possible. At the point where Faust asks Mephosto what Hell is (Chapter 9), the copyist took down an old Latin-German, German-Latin dictionary and copied out several pages of names for Hell together with their derivations. Where Faust goes on a trip to Rome and Constantinople (Chapter 18), the copyist opened up a good chronicle of the world and drew out lengthy data on European cities. He made Faust visit all of them, too. We have these two reference works as well as others which the copyist used in the same way. His procedure was so mechanical — when he drew lists from the dictionary, for example, he retained the alphabetical order — that we have little difficulty distinguishing his work from the original Faust Book.

But, just as we do not have the original Faust Book, we do not have this copy and supplementation, either. Sometime during the past four centuries it, too, was lost. However, a very conscientious copy was made of it sometime in the mid-1580's. This, the oldest version of the Faust Book which has come down to us now lies in the Duke-August Library in Wolfenbüttel, a little town just south of Brunswick. In their day, Leibniz and Lessing served as librarians there. Today the jagged Zone boundary, Germany's share of the Iron Curtain, runs just beside the town. It is on the Wolfenbüttel Manuscript that the present edition of the Faust Book is based.

THE FAUST BOOK ENTERS PRINT

The Faust Book did not really enter into German and world literature until 1587, when a very respectable Protestant publisher in Frankfurt, Johann Spiess, got his hands on the same expanded version which the scribe of the Wolfenbüttel Manuscript had used. A couple of the more salacious chapters and some of the insolent remarks were deleted, many a pious moral was drawn, numerous Christian admonitions were added, and Spiess had produced the best money-maker of the century. Although he did not get the book off his presses until the fall of 1587, two more printings were required before the year was out, in which eight new Faust tales had been added. New and further expanded editions appeared in rapid succession. In 1588, two students at the University of Tübingen turned out a Faust Book in rhymes — and, for their efforts, were promptly expelled and jailed. It is hard for us to understand the aura of danger which surrounded such a book in those days, but the perilous and forbidden blasphemies which the Faust Book was supposed to contain undoubtedly contributed to its unprecedented popularity.

Translations appeared in rapid succession in almost every

European tongue. The Dutch version of 1600 was the first to contain woodcuts especially prepared for Faust's adventures. Many of them are reproduced here. Some of the translations, of course, were prepared by men who, like the author of *The Historie of the damnable life, and deserued death of Doctor Iohn Faustus,* knew just enough German to fire their imaginations. Since the first printing of this English Faust has not survived, we do not know just when it appeared (the oldest copy we have was "newly imprinted" in 1592), and we are not able to assess with any certainty the relationship of Christopher Marlowe to the translator.

It was Marlowe's famous *Tragedy of Doctor Faustus* which, returned to Germany, became the major factor in the survival of the Faust tradition in Georg Faust's homeland. Here, over two hundred years after that notorious astrologer's death — and within a few hours' walk of Wolf Wambach's Erfurt — Wolfgang Goethe transformed what had become a crude puppet farce into the representative work of Western culture.

THE FAUST FIGURE

We can call Goethe's drama *the* representative work of our modern civilization, because it still seems to be our final statement of faith in man's inborn drive: "The man who keeps on striving, he can be saved." The change which occurred between 1570 and 1770 in our attitude toward the Faust figure is equally characteristic for the development of European thought between the Middle Ages and modern times. The Faust whose urgent search for experiences in this world becomes, with Goethe, his saving quality is essentially the same wretch who, in the sixteenth-century Faust Book, is condemned to Hell along with Cain and Judas. In the 1570's Faust's quest for sufficient knowledge to work his own salvation was, like his carnal lust for Helen, the original sin of depraved mankind. By the 1770's, Faust's longing for knowledge was a force within him which, in harmony with the redeeming love of woman, drew him ever upward.

Between the sixteenth and the eighteenth centuries, Faust had become the ridiculous hero of popular German puppet plays. Since Goethe, he has remained one of the most widely used serious figures of Western literature. Different facets of his character are stressed from one work to the next, of course. Byron's *Manfred* gives expression to the author's own *Weltschmerz*. A French opera sees Faust as a romantic lover, an American short story by Stephen V. Benet, as a Yankee farmer — but he is always a sympathetic hero because he still represents for us our own "faustian" soul.

Until 1945, he was also seen as an essentially good man, however dark his drives. But in that year Thomas Mann published a novel written during the war, while his homeland was being devastated. This latest Faust no longer seems to represent Western man, but — more narrowly — the German spirit. His name is Faustus again, like the hero of the sixteenth-century Faust Book, and he undergoes experiences analogous to those of that original Faust, including final damnation. Thomas Mann's Faustus is a composer whose great ambition is to refute that noblest tribute to the goodness of mankind, Beethoven's *Ninth Symphony*. If Mann himself succeeded in refuting the greatest literary work of Beethoven's day, Goethe's optimistic *Faust,* then the treatment of the Faust figure has in our time run its full cycle, and the pessimistic statement of the sixteenth-century Faust Book may indeed be the one we prefer to accept today.

OUR *HISTORIA* AND TALE

What you are about to read represents all we know about that original novel, written sometime around 1580. All that is here is taken directly from the Wolfenbüttel Manuscript, the oldest and best version we have of the remarkable little work. Nothing has been added. Some chapters from the Wolfenbüttel Manuscript are deleted here — for the reasons discussed — and other material has been re-organized. Each of these alterations corresponds with detailed research which earlier workers and I have presented in various scholarly publications. Some of the changes

15

are of course no more than best guesses, but the end result — which lies before you — is probably just as close as we shall ever get to how the Faust Book looked when it was first written.

Several scholars have assumed that the original was in Latin — the product, then, of an academic, probably Humanist pen. Among the modern languages, English with its excellent potential for long periods and participial phrases, together with its impressive stock of Latin vocabulary, can probably approach such a style most effectively. And the style is, I think, important as a means of reproducing the somewhat stuffy, pedantic yet credulous, constantly moralizing tone of the early Faust Book. For this reason I have seen fit to dip the little novel into the slightly archaic language of Marlowe, Shakespeare, the King James Bible — and of the 1592 English Faust Book. This is, of course, to run the risk on the one hand of quaintness, on the other of embarrassing anachronisms, but I felt that the risk was worth taking. Both in England and in Germany, frequent use of Latin words and phrases was widespread around 1600 — be it to display learning or simply to mystify the reader — and I have left untranslated the numerous Latinisms from my German text.

There remains one more important difference between the original and this machine-bound copy. Four centuries back, you would have read the Faust Book on folio parchment, handwritten by a professional scribe. By 1580, of course, not only scholarly treatises were being printed, but great quantities of chapbooks for wide popular consumption as well. Your Faust Book was not in print because the people regarded it as a horrible, blasphemous account which endangered the soul of its reader. You and your tight little circle of friends — most of them students from families of the German nobility — would have been able to face such perils with a sophisticated smile as you passed the manuscript around, but still you probably would have read it with a secret hope that it might contain certain hints as to how you, too, could acquire a familiar spirit, a devil subservient to you.

HISTORIA & TALE OF

DOCTOR JOHANNES FAUSTUS

The sorcerer, wherein is described specifically and veraciously:
His entire life and death,
How he did oblige himself for a certain time unto the Devil,
And what happened to him,
And how he at last got his well-deserved reward.

Rare revelations are also included, for these examples are most useful and efficacious as a highly essential Christian warning and admonition, that the laity, in order to protect themselves from similar maculations of the most shameful sort, have especial cause to heed and to avoid such a desperate fate.

HERE BEGINNETH DOCTOR
FAUSTUS HIS *VITA* & *HISTORIA*

Of His Parentage and Youth

I

Doctor Faustus, the son of a husbandman, was born in Roda in the Province of Weimar. His parents were godfearing and Christian people with many connections in Wittemberg. A kinsman who dwelt there was a citizen and possessed of considerable wealth. He reared Faustus for the parents and kept him as his own child, for, being himself without issue, he adopted this Faustus, made him his heir, and sent him to school to study theology. Faustus, however, strayed from this godly purpose and used God's Word vainly.

Therefore we shall blame neither his parents nor his patrons, who desired only the best (as do all pious parents), nor shall we mix them into this *Historia*. For they neither witnessed nor experienced the abominations of their godless child. One thing is certain: that these parents, as was generally known in Wittemberg, were quite heartily delighted that their kinsman adopted him. When they later perceived in Faustus his excellent *ingenium* and *memoria,* it did most assuredly trouble them, just as Job in the first chapter of that Book was concerned for his children, lest they sin against the Lord. Therefore pious parents do sometimes have godless, naughty children, and I point this out because there have been many who imputed great guilt and calumny to these parents whom I would herewith pardon. Such distortions are not merely abusive. If they imply that Faustus had been taught such things by his parents, they are also slanderous. Indeed, certain charges are alleged — to wit: that his parents had permitted wantonness in his youth, and that they had not diligently held him to his studies. It is charged that, so soon as his cleverness — together with his lack of inclination to theology — was perceived, it being further public hue and cry that he was practicing magic, his family should have prevented it betimes. All such rumors are *somnia,* for the parents, being without guilt, should not be slandered. But now *ad propositum.*

Faustus was a most percipient and adroit fellow

Faustus was a most percipient and adroit fellow, qualified and inclined toward study, and he performed so well at his examination that the rectors also examined him for the *Magister* Degree. There were sixteen other candidates, to whom he proved in address, composition, and competence so superior that it was immediately concluded he had studied sufficiently, and he became *Doctor Theologiæ.* For the rest, he was also a stupid, unreasonable and vain fellow, whom, after all, his companions always called the *speculator*. He came into the worst company, for a time laid the Holy Scriptures behindst the door and under the bench, did not revere God's Word but lived crassly and godlessly in gluttony and lust (as the progress of this *Historia* will sufficiently manifest). Surely the proverb is true: what is inclined to the Devil will go to the Devil.

Furthermore, Doctor Faustus found his ilk, who dealt in Chaldean, Persian, Arabian and Greek words, *figuræ, characteres, coniurationes, incantationes;* and these things recounted were pure *Dardaniæ artes, Nigromantiæ, carmina, veneficii, vaticini, incantationes,* and whatever you care to call such books, words and names for conjuring and sorcery. They well pleased Doctor Faustus, he speculated and studied night and day in them. Soon he refused to be called a *Theologus,* but waxed a worldly man, called himself a *Doctor Medicinæ,* became an *Astrologus* and *Mathematicus* — and, for respectability, a physician. At first he helped many people with medicaments, herbs, roots, waters, receipts, and clisters. He became learned besides, well versed in the Holy Scriptures, and he knew quite accurately the Laws of Christ: he who knoweth the will of the Lord and doeth it not, he is doubly smitten. Likewise, thou shalt not tempt the Lord thy God. All this he threw in the wind and put his soul away for a time above the door sill, wherefore there shall for him be no pardon.

How Doctor Faustus Did Achieve
and Acquire Sorcery

II

As was reported above, Doctor Faustus' complexion was such that he loved what ought not be loved, and to the which his spirit did devote itself day and night, taking on eagle's wings and seeking out the very foundations of Heaven and Earth. For his prurience, insolence and folly so pricked and incited him that he at last resolved to utilize and to prove certain magical *vocabula, figuræ, characteres* and *coniurationes* in the hope of compelling the Devil to appear before him. Hence (as others also report and as indeed Doctor Faustus himself later made known) he went into a great dense forest which is called the *Spesser Wald* and is situated near Wittemberg. Toward evening, at a crossroad in these woods, he described certain circles with his staff, so that, beside twain, the two which stood above intersected a large circle. Thus in the night between nine and ten o'clock he did conjure the Devil.

Now the Devil feigned he would not willingly appear at the spot designated, and he caused such a tumult in the forest that everything seemed about to be destroyed. He blew up such a wind that the trees were bent to the very ground. Then it seemed as were the wood with devils filled, who rode along past Doctor Faustus' circle; now only their coaches were to be seen; then from the four corners of the forest something like lightning bolts converged on Doctor Faustus' circle, and a loud explosion ensued. When all this was past, it became light in the midst of the forest, and many sweet instruments, music and song could be heard. There were various dances, too, and tourneys with spears and swords. Faustus, who thought he might have tarried long

He described certain circles with his staff

enough now, considered fleeing from his circle, but finally he regained his godless and reckless resolve and persisted in his former intention, come whatever God might send.

He continued to conjure the Devil as before, and the Devil did mystify him with the following hoax. He appeared like a griffen or a dragon hovering and flattering above the circle, and when Doctor Faustus then applied his spell the beast shrieked piteously. Soon thereafter a fiery star fell right down from three or four fathoms above his head and was transformed into a glowing ball. This greatly alarmed Faustus, too. But his purpose liked him so well, and he so admired having the Devil subservient to him that he took courage and did conjure the star once, twice, and a third time, whereupon a gush of fire from the sphere shot up as high as a man, settled again, and six little lights became visible upon it. Now one little light would leap upward, now a second downward until the form of a burning man finally emerged. He walked round about the circle for a full seven or eight minutes. The entire spectacle, however, had lasted until twelve o'clock in the night. Now a devil, or a spirit, appeared in the figure of a gray friar, greeted Doctor Faustus, and asked what his desire and intent might be. Hereupon Doctor Faustus commanded that he should appear at his house and lodging at a certain hour the next morning, the which the devil for a while refused to do. Doctor Faustus conjured him by his master, however, compelling him to fulfill his desire, so that the spirit at last consented and agreed.

Here Followeth the *Disputatio* Held
by Faustus and the Spirit

III

Doctor Faustus returned home and later the same morning commanded the spirit into his chamber, who indeed appeared to hear what Doctor Faustus might desire of him (and it is most astounding that a spirit, when God withdraws his hand, can so deceive mankind). Doctor Faustus again commenced his machinations, conjured him anew, and laid before the spirit these several articles, to wit:

Firstly, that the spirit should be subservient and obedient to him in all that he might request, inquire, or expect of him, throughout Faustus' life and death.

Secondly, that the spirit would withhold no information which Faustus, in his studies, might require.

Thirdly, that the spirit would respond nothing untruthful to any of his *interrogationes*.

The spirit immediately rejected the articles, refused Faustus, and explained his reason: that he had not complete authority except in so far as he could obtain it from his lord who ruled over him. He spake: Sweet Fauste, it standeth neither within my election nor authority to fulfill thy desires, but is left to the Hellish god.

Faustus replied: What? How am I to understand thee? Art thou not thine own master?

The spirit answered: Nay.

Faustus then said to him: Sweet spirit, explain it to me then.

Doctor Faustus commanded the spirit into his chamber

Now thou shalt know, Fauste, said the spirit, that among us there is a government and sovereignty, just as on earth, for we have our rulers and governors and servants — of whom I am one — and we call our kingdom Legion. For although the banished devil Lucifer brought about his own fall through vanity and insolence, he raised up a Legion, nevertheless, and a government of devils, and we call him the Oriental Prince, for he had his sovereignty in Ascension. It is thus a sovereignty *in Meridie, Septentrione* and *Occidente* as well. Well, inasmuch as Lucifer the fallen angel now hath his sovereignty and principality beneath the Heavens, we must, on account of this transformation, betake ourselves unto mankind and serve them. But with all his power and arts man could not make Lucifer subservient, except that a spirit be sent, as I am sent. Certainly we have never revealed to men the real fundament of our dwelling place, nor our rule and sovereignty. No one knoweth what doth occur after the death of the damned human — who learneth and experienceth it.

Doctor Faustus became alarmed at this and said: Then I will not be damned for thy sake.

The spirit answered: Wilt not agree? For thee no plea. If there be no plea, thou must come with me. Thou wost it not when we hold thee. Yet come thou must with me, nor helpeth any plea: an insolent heart hath damned thee.

Then Doctor Faustus said: A pox take thee! Hence! Begone!

Even in the moment when the spirit was about to withdraw, Doctor Faustus did change his vacillating mind. He conjured the spirit to appear at the same place at vespers to hear what else he would require. The spirit granted this and disappeared from before him.

The Second *Disputatio* with the Spirit

IV

At Vespers, or at four o'clock in the evening, the flying spirit again appeared unto Faustus and proffered his obedience and subservience in all things, if so be that Faustus would tender certain articles to him in return. Would he do that, then his desires would know no want. These following were the several articles required by the spirit:

Firstly, that he, Faustus, would agree to a certain number of years, at the expiration of which he would promise and swear to be his, the spirit's, own property.

Secondly, that he would, to the further confirmation thereof, give himself over with a writ to this effect authenticated in his own blood.

Thirdly, that he would renounce the Christian Faith and defy all believers.

Should he observe all such points, every lust of his heart would be fulfilled. And (spake the spirit) thou shalt immediately be possessed of a spirit's form and powers. Puffed up with pride and arrogance, Doctor Faustus (although he did consider for a space) had got so proud and reckless that he did not want to give thought to the weal of his soul, but came to terms with the evil spirit, promised to observe all his articles, and to obey them. He supposed that the Devil might not be so black as they use to paint him, nor Hell so hot as the people say.

Doctor Faustus' Third *Colloquium* with the Spirit, Which Was Called *Mephostophiles* — Concerning Also the Pact Which These Two Made

V

Now as for the Pact, it came about in this wise. Doctor Faustus required the spirit to come before him on the next morning, commanding him to appear, so often as he might be

Doctor Faustus required the spirit to come before him in the figure, form and raiment of a Franciscan Monk

called, in the figure, form and raiment of a Franciscan Monk, and always with a little bell to give certain signals withal, in

31

order that by the sound it might be known when he was approaching. Then he asked the spirit his name, and the spirit answered: Mephostophiles. — Even in this hour did the godless man cut himself off from his God and Creator to become a liege of the abominable Devil, whereto pride, arrogance and transgression did bring and seduce him.

Afterwards, in audacity and trangression, Doctor Faustus executed a written instrument and document to the evil spirit. This was a blasphemous and horrible thing, which was found

Doctor Faustus executed a written instrument

in his lodging after he had lost his life. I will include it as a warning to all pious Christians, lest they yield to the Devil and be cheated of body and soul (as afterward his poor famulus was by Doctor Faustus to this devilish work seduced).

When these two wicked parties contracted with one another, Doctor Faustus took a penknife, pricked open a vein in his left hand (and it is the veritable truth that upon this hand were seen graven and bloody the words: *o homo fuge — id est:* o mortal fly from him and do what is right), drained his blood into a crucible, set it on some hot coals and wrote as here followeth.

Doctor Faustus' *Instrumentum,* or Devilish and Godless Writ

Obligatio

VI

I, JOHANN FAUSTUS, Dr.,

Do publicly declare with mine own hand in covenant & by power of these presents:

Whereas, mine own spiritual faculties having been exhaustively explored (including the gifts dispensed from above and graciously imparted to me), I still cannot comprehend;

And whereas, it being my wish to probe further into the matter, I do propose to speculate upon the *Elementa;*

And whereas mankind doth not teach such things;

Now therefore have I summoned the spirit who calleth himself Mephostophiles, a servant of the Hellish Prince in Orient, charged with informing and instructing me, and agreeing against a promissory instrument hereby transferred unto him to be subservient and obedient to me in all things.

I do promise him in return that, when I be fully sated of that which I desire of him, twenty-four years also being past, ended and expired, he may at such a time and in whatever manner or wise pleaseth him order, ordain, reign, rule and possess all that may be mine: body, property, flesh, blood, etc., herewith duly bound over in eternity and surrendered by covenant in mine own hand by authority and power of these presents, as well as of my mind, brain, intent, blood and will.

I do now defy all living beings, all the Heavenly Host and all mankind, and this must be.

In confirmation and contract whereof I have drawn out mine own blood for certification in lieu of a seal.

Doctor Faustus, the Adept
in the *Elementa* and in Church Doctrine

Concerning the Service that Mephostophiles
Used Toward Faustus

VII

Doctor Faustus having with his own blood and in his own hand committed such an abomination unto the spirit, it is certainly to be assumed that God and the whole Heavenly Host did turn away from him. He dwelt in the house of his good Wittemberg kinsman, who had died and in his testament bequeathed it to Doctor Faustus. With him he had a young schoolboy as famulus, a reckless lout named Christoph Wagner. Doctor Faustus' game well pleased Wagner, and his lord also flattered him by saying he would make a learned and worthy man of him. A tune like that appealed to him (youth being always more inclined toward wickedness than toward goodness).

Now Doctor Faustus, as I said, had no one in his house save his famulus and his spirit Mephostophiles, who, in his presence, always went about in the form of a friar, and whom Doctor Faustus conjured in his study, a room which he kept locked at all times. Faustus had a superfluity of victuals and provisions, for when he desired a good wine the spirit brought it to him from whatever cellars he liked (the Doctor himself was once heard to remark that he made great inroads on the cellar of his Lord the Elector of Saxony as well as those of the Duke of Bavaria and of the Bishop of Saltzburg). He likewise enjoyed cooked fare every day, for he was so cunning in sorcery that when he opened a window and named some fowl he desired, it came flying right in through the window. His spirit also brought him cooked meat of a most princely sort from the courts of the nobility in all the territories round about. The fabrics for his apparel and that of his boy (he went sumptuously clothed) the spirit also had to buy or steal by night in Nuremberg, Augsburg or Frankfurt. A similar injury was done the tanners and cobblers. In sum, it was all stolen, wickedly borrowed goods, so that Doctor Faustus' meat and clothing was very respectable, but godless. Indeed Christ our Lord doth through John call the Devil a thief and a murderer, and that is what he is.

The devil also promised to give Faustus twenty-five Crowns a week, which amounts to 1,300 Crowns a year, and that was his year's emolument.

Concerning Doctor Faustus' Intended Marriage

VIII

While he lived thus day in and day out like an Epicure — or like a sow — with faith neither in God, Hell nor the Devil, Doctor Faustus' *aphrodisia* did day and night so prick him that he desired to enter matrimony and take a wife. He questioned his spirit in this regard, who was to be sure an enemy of the matrimonial estate as created and ordained by God.

The spirit answered: Well, what is thy purpose with thyself? *Viz.,* had Faustus forgot his commitment, and would he not hold to the promise wherein he had vowed enmity to God and mankind? If so, then neither by chance nor by intent dare he enter matrimony.

For a man cannot serve two masters (spake the devil), God and us, too. Matrimony is a work of the Lord God. We, who take our profit from all that pertains to and derives from adultery and fornication, are opposed to it. Wherefore, Fauste, look thou to it: shouldst thou promise to wed, thou shalt then most assuredly be torn into little pieces by us. Sweet Fauste, judge for thyself what unquiet, antipathy, anger and strife result from matrimony.

Doctor Faustus considered various sides of the matter, his monk constantly presenting objections. At last he said: Well, I will wed, let come of it what may!

When Faustus had uttered this resolve, a storm wind did fall upon his house and seemed about to destroy it. All the doors leapt from their hooks, and at the same instant his house was quite filled with heat, just as if it were about to burn away into pure ashes. Doctor Faustus took to his heels down the stair, but a man caught him up and cast him back into the parlor with such a force that he could move neither hand nor foot. Round about him everywhere sprang up fire. He thought he would be burned alive, and he screamed to his spirit for help, promising to live in accordance with every wish, counsel and precept. Then

Lo, then will I tickle thy lust otherwise

the Devil himself appeared unto him, so horrible and malformed that Faustus could not look upon him.

Satan said: Now tell me, of what purpose art thou?

Doctor Faustus gave him short answer, admitting that he had not fulfilled his promise in that he had not deemed it to extend so far, and he did request Grace.

Satan answered him equally curtly: Then be henceforth steadfast. I tell thee, be steadfast.

After this, the spirit Mephostophiles came to him and said unto him: If thou are henceforth steadfast in thy commitment, lo, then will I tickle thy lust otherwise, so that in thy days thou wilt wish naught else than this — namely: if thou canst not live chastely, then will I lead to thy bed any day or night whatever woman thou seest in this city or elsewhere. Whoever might please thy lust, and whomever thou might desire in lechery, she shall abide with thee in such a figure and form.

Doctor Faustus was so intrigued by this that his heart trembled with joys and his original proposal rued him. And he did then come into such libidinousness and dissipation that he yearned day and night after the figure of the beautiful women in such excellent forms, dissipating today with one devil and having another on his mind tomorrow.

Doctor Faustus' *Quæstio*
of His Spirit Mephostophiles

IX

Now after Doctor Faustus had for a time carried on such a very fine matrimony with the Devil (as was reported above), his spirit committed unto him a great book containing all manner of sorcery and *nigromantia,* wherein he indulged himself in addition to his devilish wedlock (these *dardaniæ artes* later being found with his famulus and son Christoph Wagner). Soon his curiosity did prick him and he summoned his spirit Mephostophiles, with whom he desired to converse and to whom he said: Tell me, my servant, what manner of spirit art thou?

The spirit answered and spake: This *disputatio* and question, if I am to elucidate it for thee, my Lord Fauste, will move thee somewhat to discontent and to contemplation. Moreover, thou ought not have asked such of me, for it toucheth on our arcana. — But I must obey thee.

Thou shalt know therefore that the Banished Angel at the time of his fall was still graciously and kindly disposed toward man, who had just been created. But soon the leaf did turn and Lucifer, become the enemy of God and all mankind, did pre-

sume to work all manner of tyranny upon men — as is every day
manifest when one falleth to his death; another hangeth, drown-
eth or stabbeth himself; a third is stabbed, driven mad, and the
like other cases which thou might have observed. Because the
first man was created so perfect by God, the Devil did begrudge
him such. He beset Adam and Eve and brought them with all
their seed into sin and out of the Grace of God. Such, sweet
Fauste, is the onslaught and tyranny of Satan. Likewise did he
unto Cain. He caused the people of Israel to worship him, to
sacrifice unto strange gods and to go lustfully in unto the heathen
women. It was one of our spirits who pursued Saul and drave
him into madness, pricking him on til he took his own life.
Another spirit is amongst us, Asmodeus, who slew seven men in
lechery. Then there is the spirit Dagon, who caused 30,000 men
to fall way from God, so that they were slain and the Ark of God
was captured. And Belial, who did prick David's heart that he
began to number the people, and 60,000 perished. It was one of
us who did send Solomon awhoring after false gods. Without
number are our spirits that do insinuate themselves among men
and cause them to fall. To this very day we still distribute ourselves over all the world, using every sort of guile and rascality,
driving men away from the Faith and urging them on to sin and
wickedness, that we may strengthen ourselves as best we can
against Jesus by plaguing his followers unto death. We possess,
to be sure, the hearts of the kings and rulers of this world, hard-
ening them against the teachings of Jesus and of his apostles and
followers.

Doctor Faustus answered and spake: So hast thou possessed
me also? Sweet fellow, tell me the truth.

The spirit answered: Well why not? As soon as we looked
upon thy heart and saw with what manner of thoughts thou
didst consort, how thou couldst neither use nor get another than
the Devil for such an intent and purpose, lo, we then made those
thoughts and strivings yet more impious and bold, and so pru-
rient that thou hadst no rest by day nor by night, all thine aspira-

tions and endeavors being directed toward the accomplishment of sorcery. Even while thou didst conjure us, we were amaking thee so wicked and so audacious that thou hadst let the very Devil fetch thee before thou hadst forsaken thy purpose. Afterward, we encouraged thee yet further until we had planted it into thy heart not to falter in thy cause until thou hadst a spirit subservient unto thee. In the end, we persuaded thee to yield thyself to us finally and with body and soul. All this, Lord Fauste, canst thou learn from thyself.

It is true, quoth Doctor Faustus, there is no turning from my way now. I have ensnared myself. Had I kept god-fearing thoughts, and held to God in prayer, not allowing the Devil so to strike root within me, then had I not suffered such injury in body and soul. Ay, what have I done, etc.

The spirit made answer: Look thou to it.

Thus did Doctor Faustus take his despondent leave.

A *Disputatio* Concerning the Prior State
of the Banished Angels

X

Doctor Faustus again undertook a discourse with his spirit, asking: How, then, did thy master, Lucifer, come to fall?

This time, Mephostophiles asked of him a three-day prorogation, but on the third day the spirit gave him this answer: My Lord Lucifer (who is so called on account of his banishment from the clear light of Heaven) was in Heaven an angel of God and a cherub. He beheld all works and creations of God in Heaven and was himself with such honor, title, pomp, dignity and prominence as to be the exemplary creature before God, in great perfection of wisdom, yea in such brilliance that he outshone all other creatures and was an ornament beyond all other works of God, gold and precious stones, even the sun and stars. For so soon as God created him He placed him upon the Mount of God as a sovereign prince, and he was perfect in all his ways.

But so soon as he rose up in insolence and vanity and would exalt himself above Orient he was driven out from the House of Heaven, thrust down into fiery brimstone which is eternally unextinguished and tormenteth him forever. He had been honored with the crown of all Heavenly pomp. But since he sat in spiteful council against God, God sat upon His Throne of Judgement and condemned him to Hell, whence he can never more rise up.

Doctor Faustus, having heard the spirit concerning these things, did now speculate upon many different tenets and justifications. He went in silence from the spirit into his chamber, laid himself upon his bed and began bitterly to weep and to sigh, and to cry out in his heart. For the account by the spirit caused him this time to consider how the Devil and Banished Angel had been so excellently honored of God, and how, if he had not been so rebellious and arrogant against God, he would have had an eternal Heavenly essence and residence, but was now by God eternally banished.

Faustus spake: O woe is me and ever woe! Even so will it come to pass with me also, nor will my fate be the more bearable, for I am likewise God's creature, and my insolent flesh and blood have set me body and soul into perdition, enticed me with my reason and mind so that I as a creature of God am strayed from Him and have let the Devil seduce me to bind myself unto him with body and soul, wherefore I can hope no more for Grace, but must needs be, like Lucifer, banished into perpetual damnation and lamentation. Ah woe and ever woe! To what perils I am exposing myself! What is my purpose with myself? O, that I were never born!

Thus did Doctor Faustus complain, but he would not take faith, nor hope that he might be through penitence brought back to the Grace of God. For if he had thought: The Devil doth now take on such a color that I must look up to Heaven. Lo, I will turn about again and call upon God for Grace and Forgiveness, for to sin no more is a great penance. Then Faustus would have betaken himself to church and followed Holy Doctrine, thereby offering the Devil resistance. Even if he had been compelled to yield up his body here, his soul would nevertheless have been saved. But he became doubtful in all his tenets and opinions, having no faith and little hope.

A *Disputatio* Concerning Hell,
How It Was Created and Fashioned;
Concerning Also the Torments in Hell

XI

Doctor Faustus had, no doubt, contrition in his heart at all times. It was a concern for how he had endangered his own salvation when he plighted himself to the Devil for the sake of temporal things. But his contrition was the contrition and penance of Cain and Judas. Indeed there was contrition in his heart, but he despaired of the Grace of God, it seeming to him an impossibility to gain God's favor: like unto Cain, who also despaired, saying his sins were greater than could be forgiven him. It was the same with Judas.

And it was the same with Doctor Faustus. I suppose he looked up to Heaven, but his eyes discerned naught therein. They say that he dreamt of the Devil and of Hell. That means that when he recalled his transgressions he could not help thinking that frequent and much disputation, inquiry, and discourse with the spirit would bring him to such a fear of the consequences of sin that he would be able to mend his ways, repent his sins, and sin no more.

Thus Doctor Faustus again decided to hold discourse and a colloquium with the spirit, asking him: What is Hell; further,

45

how Hell was created and constituted; thirdly, about the manner of wailing and lamentation of the damned in Hell; and fourthly, whether the damned could come again into the favor of God and be released from Hell.

Doctor Faustus had, no doubt, contrition in his heart at all times

The spirit gave answer to none of these questions or articles, but spake: As concerns thy purpose, Lord Fauste, thy *disputatio* on Hell and Hell's effects on man, thy desire for elucidation — I say to thee: what is thy purpose with thyself?

If thou couldst ascend directly into Heaven, yet would I fling thee down into Hell again, for thou art mine, walking my path toward Hell even in thy many questions about Hell. Sweet Fauste, desist. Inquire of other matters. Believe me, my account will bring thee into such remorse, despondency, pensiveness, and anxiety that thou wilt wish thou hadst never posed this question. My judgement and advice remains: desist from this purpose.

Doctor Faustus spake: And I will know it or I will not live, and thou must tell it me.

Very well, quoth the spirit, I will tell thee. It costeth me little grief.

Thou wouldst know what Hell is, but the mortal soul is such that all thy speculations can never comprehend Hell, nor canst thou conceive the manner of place where the Wrath of God is stored. The origin and structure is God's Wrath, and it hath many titles and designations, as: House of Shame, Abyss, Gullet, Pit, also *Dissensio*. For the souls of the damned are also shamed, scorned and mocked by God and His Blessed Ones, that they are thus confined in the House of the Abyss and Gullet. For Hell is an insatiate Pit and Gullet which ever gapeth after the souls which shall not be damned, desiring that they, too, might be seduced and damned. This is what thou must understand, good Doctor.

So soon as my master was fallen, and even at that moment, Hell was ready for him and received him. It is a Darkness where Lucifer is all banished and bound with chains of darkness, here committed that he may be held for Judgement. Naught may be found there but fumes, fire and the stench of sulphur. But we devils really cannot know in what form and wise Hell is created, either, nor how it be founded and constructed by God, for it hath neither end nor bottom.

That is my first and second report, which thou hast required of me. For the third, thou didst conjure me and demand of me a report as to what manner of wailing and lamentation the damned will find in Hell. Perchance, my Lord Fauste, thou shouldst consult the Scriptures (they being withheld from me). But now even as the aspect and description of Hell is terrible, so to be in it is an unbearable, acute agony. Inasmuch as I have already given account of the former, thy hellish speculations on the latter will I also satisfy with a report. The damned will encounter all the circumstances which I recounted afore, for what I say is true:

The pit of Hell, like womb of woman, and earth's belly, is never sated. Nevermore will an end or cessation occur. They will cry out and lament their sin and wickedness, the damned and hellish hideousness of the stench of their own afflictions. There will then be at last a calling out, a screaming and a wailing out unto God, with woe, trembling, whimpering, yelping, screaming and pain and affliction, with howling and weeping. Well, should they not scream woe and tremble and whimper, being outcast, with all Creation and all the children of God against them, bearing perpetual ignominy while the blessed enjoy eternal honor? And the woe and trembling of some will be greater than that of others, for, as sins are not equal, neither are the torments and agonies the same.

We spirits shall be freed. We have hope of being saved. But the damned will lament the insufferable cold, the unquenchable fire, the unbearable darkness, stench, the aspect of the devils, and the eternal loss of anything good. Oh, they will lament with weeping of eyes, gnashing of teeth, stench in their noses, moaning in their throats, terror in their ears, trembling in their hands and feet. They will devour their tongues for great pain. They will wish for death, would gladly die, but cannot, for death will flee from them. Their torment and agony will wax hourly greater and acuter.

There, my Lord Fauste, thou hast thy third answer, which is consonant with the first and second. Thy fourth question pertaineth to God: whether He will receive the damned into His Grace again. Thanks to thine other, related inquiries, and mine own views concerning Hell and its nature, how it was created of God's Wrath, we have been able to clarify certain fundamentals in advance. Thou shalt now receive one further, specific account (in spite of the fact that it will be in direct violation of thy contract and vow).

Thy last question is whether the damned in Hell can ever come again into the favor and Grace of God, and mine answer is: No. For all who are in Hell are there because God banished them there, and they must therefore burn perpetually in God's Wrath and severity, must remain and abide in a place where no hope can be believed. Yea, if they could eventually gain the Grace of God (as we spirits, who always have hope and are in constant expectancy) they would take cheer, and sigh in anticipation. But the damned have even as little hope as have the devils in Hell of transcending their banishment and disgrace. They can have no more hope of salvation than can they hope for a twinkling of light in Hell's darkness, for refreshment with a drink of water in hellfire's heat and anguish, or for warmth in Hell's cold. Neither their pleading, nor their prayer, their crying nor their sighing will be heard, and their conscience will not let them forget.

Emperors, kings, princes, counts and other such regents will lament: had they but not lived all in violence and lust, then they might come into the favor of God. A rich man: had he but not been a miser. A frivolous man: had he but not been vainglorious. An adulterer and philanderer: had he but not indulged in lechery, adultery and fornication. A drunkard, glutton, gambler, blasphemer, perjurer, thief, highwayman, murderer, and their ilk: had I but not filled my belly daily with sumptuousness, pleasure and superfluity of drink and victual, had I but not cheated, blasphemed God in my heart, had I but not scolded wickedly and wantonly against God at every opportunity, had I but not borne false witness, stolen, sacked, murdered, robbed, then perhaps I could still hope for Grace. But my sins are too great and cannot be forgiven me, wherefore I must suffer this hellish torment. Hence may I, damned man, be sure that there is no Grace for me.

Let it be understood then, my Lord Fauste, that the damned man — or the soul, if you will — can no more attain Grace than can he hope for an end to his sufferings or a tide wherein he might perchance be removed from such anguish. Why, if they could be given the hope of dipping water day by day from the sea at the sea shore until the sea were dry, then that would be a redemption. Or if there were a sandheap as high as Heaven from which a bird coming every other year might bear away but one little grain at a time, and they would be saved after the whole heap were consumed, then that would be a hope. But God will never take any thought of them. They will lie in Hell like unto the bones of the dead. Death and their conscience will gnaw on them. Their firm belief and faith in God — oh they will at last acquire it — will go unheeded, and no thought will be taken of them. Thou thinkest perhaps that the damned soul might cover itself over and conceal itself in Hell until God's Wrath might at last subside, and thou hast the hope that there might come a release if thou but persist in the aim of hope that God might still take thought of thee — even then there will be no salvation. There will come a time when the mountains collapse, and when all the stones at the bottom of the sea are dry, and all the raindrops have washed the earth away. It is possible to conceive of an elephant or a camel entering into a needle's eye, or of counting all the raindrops. But there is no conceiving of a time of hope in Hell.

Thus, in short, my Lord Fauste, hast thou my fourth and last report. And thou shalt know that if thou ask me more of such things another time thou shalt get no audience from me, for I am not obligated to tell thee such things. Therefore leave me in peace with further such probings and *disputationes*.

Again Doctor Faustus departed from the spirit all melancholy, confused and full of doubt, thinking now this way now that, and pondering on these things day and night. But there was no constancy in him, for the Devil had hardened his heart and blinded him. And indeed when he did succeed in being alone to contemplate the Word of God, the Devil would dizen himself in the form of a beautiful woman, embrace him, dissipating with him, so that he soon forgot the Divine Word and threw it to the wind.

DOCTOR FAUSTUS HIS *HISTORIA*
HERE FOLLOWETH THE SECOND
PART ADVENTURES & SUNDRY
QUESTIONS

His Almanacs and Horoscopes

XII

Doctor Faustus, being no longer able to obtain answers from his spirit concerning godly matters, now had to rest content and desist from this purpose. It was in those days that he set about making almanacs and became a good *astronomus* and *astrologus*. He gained so much learning and experience from the spirit concerning horoscopes that all which he did contrive and write won the highest praise among all the *mathematici* of that day (as is, after all, common knowledge now). His horoscopes, which he sent to great lords and princes, always were correct, for he contrived them according to the advice of his spirit as to what would come to pass in the future, all such matters falling duly out even as he had presaged them.

His tables and almanacs were praised above others because he set down naught in them but what did indeed come to pass. When he presaged fogs, wind, snow, precipitation, etc., these things were all quite certain. His almanacs were not as those of some unskilled *astrologi* who know of course that it gets cold in the winter, and hence forecast freezes, or that it will be hot in the summer, and predict thunderstorms. Doctor Faustus always calculated his tables in the manner described above, setting what should come to pass, specifying the day and the hour and especially warning the particular districts — this one with famine, that one with war, another with pestilence, and so forth.

A *Disputatio,* or Inquiry Concerning
the Art of *Astronomia,* or *Astrologia*

XIII

One time after Doctor Faustus had been contriving and producing such horoscopes and almanacs for about two years he did ask his spirit about the nature of *astronomia* or *astrologia* as practiced by the *mathematici.*

The spirit gave answer, saying: My Lord Fauste, it is so ordained that the ancient haruspices and modern stargazers are unable to forecast anything particularly certain, for these are deep mysteries of God which mortals cannot plumb as we spirits can, who hover in the air beneath Heaven where we can see and mark what God hath predestined. Yes, we are ancient spirits, experienced in the Heavenly movements. Why, Lord Fauste, I could make thee a perpetual calender for the setting of horoscopes and almanacs or for nativity investigations one year after the other. — Thou hast seen that I have never lied to thee. Now it is true that the Patriarchs, who lived for five and six hundred years, did comprehend the fundamentals of this art and become very adept. For when such a great number of years elapse a luni-solar period is completed, and the older generation can apprise the younger of it. Except for that, all green inexperienced *astrologi* have to set up their horoscopes arbitrarily according to conjecture.

A *Disputatio* and False Answer Which the Spirit Gave to Doctor Faustus

XIV

The spirit, finding Doctor Faustus all sorrowful and melancholy, did ask him what his grievance might be, and what was on his mind. When he saw that Doctor Faustus would give him no answer, he became importunate and pressing, demanding to know the exact nature of Faustus' thoughts, so that he might be of some aid to him if at all possible.

Doctor Faustus answered, saying: Well, I have taken thee unto me as a servant, and thy service doth cost me dear enough. Yet I cannot have my will of thee, as would be proper of a servant.

The spirit spake: My Lord, thou knowest that I have never opposed thee, but have ever humored thee. Except on one occasion, when I withheld information on one specific subject and under certain express terms, I have ever been submissive unto thee. Now why wilt thou not reveal thy desires? What is in thy mind?

With such talk the spirit stole away the heart of Faustus, and he confessed that he had been wondering how God created the world, and about the original birth of mankind. The spirit now gave Faustus a godless, unchristian and childish account and report on this subject, saying:

The world, my Lord Fauste, hath never experienced birth and will never know death, and the human race has always existed. There is not any origin or beginning of things. The earth subsists, as always, of itself. The sea arose from the earth, and the two got along so very well that one would think they had carried on a conversation in which the land had required his realm from the sea, the fields, meadows, woods, grass and trees; and that the sea had likewise demanded his own realm of water with the fish and all else therein. Now they did concede to God the creation of mankind and of Heaven, and this is the way they finally became subservient to God. Thou wilt observe that I have explained how from one realm there finally arose four: air, fire, water, and earth. I know none other, nor briefer, way of instructing thee.

Doctor Faustus speculated on these things but could not comprehend them, for in the first chapter of Genesis he had read how Moses had told it otherwise. For this reason, he made no further comment.

How Doctor Faustus Traveled
Down to Hell

XV

With each passing day, Doctor Faustus' end drew closer, and he was now come into his eighth year, having been for the most part of the time engaged in inquiry, study, questioning and *disputationes*. In these days he again did dream of Hell, and it caused him again to summon his servant, the spirit Mephostophiles, demanding that he call his own lord, Belial, unto him. The spirit agreed to do this, but instead of Belial a devil was sent who called himself Beelzebub, a flying spirit reigning beneath Heaven. When he asked what Doctor Faustus desired of him, Faustus asked whether it could not be arranged for a spirit to conduct him into Hell and out again, so that he might see and mark the nature, fundament, quality and substance of Hell.

Yes, answered Beelzebub, I will come at midnight and fetch thee.

Well, when it got pitch dark Beelzebub appeared unto him, bearing upon his back a bone chair which was quite enclosed round about. Here Doctor Faustus took a seat, and they flew away. Now hear how the Devil did mystify and gull him, so that he had no other notion than that he really had been in Hell.

He bare him into the air, where Doctor Faustus fell asleep just as if he were lying in a bath of warm water. Soon afterward he came upon a mountain of a great island, high above which sulphur, pitch and flashes of fire blew and crashed with such a tumult that Doctor Faustus awoke when his devilish dragon swooped down into the abyss. Although all was violently burning round about him, he sensed neither heat nor fire, but rather little spring breezes as in May. Then he heard many different instruments whose music was exceeding sweet, but, as bright as shone the fire, he could see no one playing, nor durst he ask, questions having been strictly forbidden him.

In these days he again did dream of Hell

Meanwhile, three more devilish dragons had flown up alongside Beelzebub. They were just like him and they went flying along ahead of him as he penetrated further into the abyss. Now a great flying stag with mighty antlers and many points came at Doctor Faustus and would have dashed him off his chair and down into the abyss. It frightened him greatly, but the three dragons flying ahead repulsed the hart. When he was better come down into the *spelunca,* he could see hovering about him a great multitude of serpents and snakes, the latter being unspeakably big. Flying lions came to his aid this time. They wrestled and struggled with the great snakes until they conquered them, so that he passed through safely and well.

When Doctor Faustus had attained a greater depth, he saw a huge, flying, angry bull come forth out of a hole which might have been an old gate. Bellowing and raging, he charged Faustus, goring his seat with such a force as to overturn pavilion, dragon and Faustus, who now did fall off from his chair into the abyss, down and down, screaming woe and waily and thinking: All is over now. He could no longer see his spirit, but at last an old wrinkled ape caught him up as he fell, held him and saved him. But then a thick dark fog fell upon Hell, so that he could not see anything at all until presently a cloud opened up, out of which climbed two big dragons pulling a coach along after them. The old ape was setting Faustus upon it when there arose such a storm wind with terrible thunder claps and stench of sulphur and quaking of the mountain or abyss that Faustus thought he must faint away and die.

He was indeed enveloped in a deep darkness for about a quarter of an hour, during which time he had no perception of the dragons or of the coach, but he did have a sensation of movement. Again the thick dark fog disappeared, and he could see his steeds and coach. Down the abyss shot such multitude of lightning and flames upon his head that the boldest man — not to mention Faustus — would have trembled for fear. The next thing he perceived was a great turbid body of water. His dragons entered it and submerged. Yet Faustus felt no water at all, but great heat and radiance instead. The current and waves beat upon him until he again lost both steeds and coach and went falling deeper and deeper into the terror of the water. At last he found himself upon a high, pointed crag and here he sat, feeling half dead.

He looked about, but as he was able to see and hear no one, he began gazing on down into the abyss. A little breeze arose. All around him there was naught but water. He thought to himself: What shalt thou do now, being forsaken even by the spirits of Hell? Why thou must hurl thyself either into the water or into the abyss. At this thought he fell into a rage, and in a mad, crazy despair he leapt into the fiery hole, calling out as he cast himself in: Now, spirits, accept my offering. I have earned it. My soul hath caused it.

Well, just at the moment when he hurled himself head over heels and went tumbling down, such a frightful loud tumult and banging assailed his ears, and the mountainpeak shook so furiously that he thought many big cannons must have been set off, but he had only come to the bottom of Hell. Here were many worthy personages in a fire: emperors, kings, princes and lords, many thousand knights and men-at-arms. A cool stream ran along at the edge of the fire, and here some were drinking, refreshing themselves, and bathing, but some were fleeing from its cold, back into the fire. Doctor Faustus stepped up, thinking he might seize one of the damned souls, but even when he thought he had one in his hand it would vanish. On account of the intense heat, he knew he could not stay in this vicinity, and he was seeking some way out when his spirit Beelzebub came with the pavilion. Doctor Faustus took a seat and away they soared, for he could not long have endured the thunderclaps, fog, fumes, sulphur, water, cold and heat, particularly since it was compounded with wailing, weeping and moaning of woe, anguish and pain.

Now Doctor Faustus had not been at home for a long while. His famulus felt sure that, if he had achieved his desire of seeing Hell, he must have seen more than he had bargained for and would never come back. But even while he was thinking thus, Doctor Faustus, asleep in his pavilion, came flying home in the night and was cast, still asleep, into his bed. When he awoke early the next morning and beheld the light of dawn, he felt exactly as if he had been imprisoned for some time in a dark tower. At a somewhat later date, he became acquainted only with the fire of Hell, and with the effects of those flames, but now he lay in bed trying to recollect what he had seen in Hell.

At first he was firmly convinced that he had been there and had seen it, but then he began to doubt himself, and assumed that the Devil had charmed a vision before his eyes. — And this is true, for he had not seen Hell, else he would not have spent the rest of his life trying to get there. This history and account of what he saw in Hell — or in a vision — was written down by Doctor Faustus himself and afterwards found in his own handwriting upon a piece of paper in a locked book.

How Doctor Faustus Journeyed Up
into the Stars

XVI

This record was also found among his possessions, having been composed and indited in his own hand and addressed to one of his close companions, a physic in Leipzig named Jonas Victor. The contents were as followeth:

Most dear Lord, and Brother,

I yet remember, as ye no doubt do, too, our school days in Wittemberg, where ye at first devoted yourself to *medicina, astronomia, astrologia, geometria,* so that ye are now a *mathematicus* and *physicus.* But I was not like unto you. I, as well ye know, did study *theologia* — although I nevertheless became your equal in the arts ye studied, too.

Now, as to your request that I report some few matters unto you and give you my advice: I, neither being accustomed to denying you aught, nor having ever refused to report aught to you, am still your servant, whom ye shall ever find and know to be such. I do express my gratitude for the honor and praise which ye accord me. In your epistle ye make mention of mine Ascension into Heaven, among the stars, for ye have heard about it, and ye write requesting that I might inform you whether it be so or not, sithence such a thing doth seem to you quite impossible. Ye remark in addition that it must have occurred with the aid of the Devil or of sorcery. "Ay, how wilt thou bet, Fritz!" quoth the clown to the Emperor when asked if he had sullied his breeches. — Well, whatever means might have been used, it hath finally been accomplished, and of this *figura, actus* and event I can make you the following report:

One night I could not go to sleep, but lay thinking about my almanacs and horoscopes and about the properties and arrangements in the Heavens, how man — or some of the physics — hath measured those ornaments and would interpret them, even though he cannot really visualize such things and must hence base his interpretations and calculations quite arbitrarily on books and the tenets in them. While in such thoughts, I heard a loud blast of wind go against my house. It threw open my shutters, my chamber door and all else, so that I was not a little astonished. Right afterward I heard a roaring voice saying:

Get thee up! Thy heart's desire, intent and lust shalt thou see.

I made answer: If it be possible for me to see that which hath just been the object of my thoughts and wishes, then I am well content.

He did answer again, saying: Then look out at thy window where thou canst see our carriage.

That I did, and I saw a coach with two dragons come flying down. The coach was illuminated with the flames of Hell, and inasmuch as the moon shone in the sky that night I could see my steeds as well. These creatures had mottled brown and white wings and the same color back; their bellies, however, were of a greenish hue with yellow and white flecks.

The voice spake again: Well get thee in and be off!

I answered: I will follow thee, but only on condition that I may ask any question I like.

Good, he answered, be it then in this instance permitted thee.

So I climbed up onto my casement, jumped down into my

63

carriage, and off I went, the flying dragons drawing me ever upward; and it did seem a miracle that the coach really had four wheels that crunched right along as if I were journeying over land. — To be sure, the wheels did gush forth streams of fire as they whirled around.

The higher I ascended, the darker did the world become, and when I would look down into the world from the Heavens above, it was exactly as if I were gazing into a dark hole from bright daylight. In the midst of such upward shooting and soaring, my servant and spirit came whirring along and took a seat beside me in the coach.

I said to him: My Mephostophiles, what is to become of me now?

Let such thoughts neither confuse thee nor impede thee, spake he and drave on higher upward.

Now Will I Tell You What I Did See

XVII

Departing on a Tuesday, and returning on a Tuesday, I was out one week, during which time I neither slept nor did feel any sleep in me. Incidentally, I remained quite invisible throughout the journey. On the first morning, at break of day, I said to my Mephostophiles:

I suppose thou dost know how far we are come (now as long as I was up there I knew neither hunger nor thirst, but I could well observe only by looking back at the world that I was come a good piece this night).

Mephostophiles said: In faith, my Fauste, thou art now come forty-seven mile up into the sky.

During the remainder of the day I discovered that I could look down upon the world and make out many kingdoms, principalities and seas. I could discern the worlds of Asia, Africa and Europe, and while at this altitude I said unto my servant:

Now point out to me and instruct me as to the names of these various lands and realms.

This he did, saying: This over here on the left is Hungary. Lo, there is Prussia. Across there is Sicily — Poland — Denmark

— Italy — Germany. Now tomorrow shalt thou inspect Asia and Africa and canst see Persia, Tartary, India and Arabia. — But just look, right now the wind is changing and we can observe Pommerania, Muscovy and Prussia. See, there is Poland — and Germany again — Hungary — and Austria.

On the third day I did look down into Major and Minor Turkey, Persia, India and Africa. I saw Constantinople before me and, in the Persian and Constantinopolitan Sea, many ships with war troops shuttling busily back and forth. Constantinople looked so small that there appeared to be no more than three houses there, with people not a span long.

Now I departed in July when it was very hot, and, as I looked now this way and now that, toward the East, South and North, I observed how it was raining at one place, thundering at another, how the hail did fall here while at another place the weather was fair. In fine, I saw all things in the world as they do usually come to pass.

After I had been up there for a week, I began to observe what was above me, watching from a distance how the Heavens did move and roll around so fast that they seemed about to fly asunder into many thousand pieces, the cloud sphere cracking so violently as if it were about to burst and break the world open. The Heavens were so bright that I could not perceive anything any higher up, and it was so hot that I should have burned to a crisp had my servant not charmed a breeze up for me. The cloud sphere which we see down there in the world is as solid and thick as a masonry wall, but it is of one piece and as clear as crystal. The rain, which originates there and then falls upon the earth, is so clear that we could see ourselves reflected in it.

Now this cloud sphere moveth in the Heavens with such a force that it runneth from East to West despite the fact that sun, moon and stars strive against it, so that the momentum of the cloud sphere doth indeed drive sun, moon and stars along with it. Thus we see how and why these bodies must proceed from East to West. Down in our world it doth appear — and I thought so, too — that the sun is no bigger than the head of a barrel. But it is in fact much bigger than the whole world: for I could discover no end to it at all. At night, when the sun goeth down, the moon must take on the sun's light, this being why the moon shineth so bright at night. And directly beneath Heaven there is so much light that even at night it is daytime in Heaven — this even though the earth remaineth quite dark. Thus I saw more than I had desired. One of the stars, for example, was larger than half the world. A planet is as large as the world. And, in the aery sphere, there I beheld the spirits which dwell beneath Heaven.

While descending, I did look down upon the world again, and it was no bigger than the yolk of an egg. Why, to me the world seemed scarcely a span long, but the oceans looked to be twice that size. Thus, on the evening of the seventh day did I arrive home again, and I slept for three days on a row. I have disposed my almanacs and horoscopes in accordance with my observations, and I did not wish to withhold this fact from you. Now inspect your books and see whether the matter is not in accordance with my vision.

And accept my cordial greetings,

Dr. Faustus
The astroseer.

Doctor Faustus' Third Journey

XVIII

It was in his sixteenth year that Doctor Faustus undertook a tour or a pilgrimage, instructing his servant that he should conduct and convey him whithersoever he would go. He journeyed invisible down to Rome, where he went unseen into the Pope's Palace and beheld all the servants and courtiers and the many sorts of dishes and fine foods that were being served.

For shame! he remarked to his spirit. Why did not the Devil make a Pope of me?

Yes, Doctor Faustus found all there to be his ilk in arrogance, pride, much insolence, transgression, gluttony, drunkenness, whoring, adultery and other fine blessings of the Pope and his rabble. This caused Doctor Faustus to observe:

Methought I were the Devil's own swine, but he will let me fatten for a long while yet. These swine in Rome are already fatted and ready to roast and boil.

Since he had heard much of Rome, he remained for three days and nights in the Pope's Palace, using his sorcery to make himself invisible. Now hear ye the adventures and the art which he used in the Pope's Palace.

The good Lord Faustus, having had little good meat and drink for some time, came and stood invisible before the Pope's board, even as he was about to eat. The Pope crossed himself before taking meat, and at that moment Doctor Faustus did blow hard into his face. Every time the Pope crossed himself, Faustus would blow into his face again. Once he laughed aloud, so that it was audible in the whole hall; again, he did weep most convincingly. The servants knew not what this might be, but the Pope told his people it was a damned soul of which he had exacted penance and which was now begging for absolution. Doctor Faustus enjoyed this very much, for such mystifications well pleased him, too.

When the last course finally arrived and was set before the Pope, Doctor Faustus, feeling his own hunger, raised up his hands, and instantly all the courses and fine dishes together with their platters flew right into them. Together with his spirit he then rushed away to a mountain in Rome called the Capitolium, there to dine with great relish. Later he sent his spirit back with an order to fetch the daintiest wines from the Pope's table together with the finest goblets and flaggons.

When the Pope found out how many things had been stolen from him, he caused all the bells to be rung throughout the entire night and had mass and petition held for the departed souls. In anger toward one departed soul, however, he formally condemned it to purgatory with bell, book and candle. As for Doctor Faustus, he accepted the Pope's meat and drink as an especial dispensation. The silver was found in his house after his death.

At midnight, when he was sated with the victuals, he bestrode a horse and flew off to Constantinople. Here Doctor Faustus viewed the Turkish Emperor's might, power, brilliance and court entourage for a few days. One evening when the Emperor sat at table Doctor Faustus performed for him an apish play and spectacle. Great tongues of fire burst up in the hall, and when everyone was hastening to quench them, it commenced to thunder and lighten. Such a spell was cast upon the Turkish Emperor that he could not arise, nor could he be carried out of there. The hall became as bright as the very homeland of the sun, and Faustus's spirit, in the figure, ornaments and trappings of a Pope, stepped before the Emperor, saying:

Hail Emperor, so full of grace that I, thy Mahomet do appear unto thee! Saying nothing more, he disappeared.

This hoax caused the Emperor to fall down upon his knees, calling out unto Mahomet and praising him that he had been so gracious as to appear before him.

The next morning, Doctor Faustus went into the Emperor's castle, where the Turk has his wives or whores, and where no one is permitted except gelded boys who wait upon the women. He charmed this castle with such a thick fog that naught could be seen. Now Doctor Faustus transformed himself as had his spirit before, but posed as Mahomet himself, and he did reside for a while in this castle, the mist remaining throughout his stay, and the Turk during this same period admonishing his people to perform many rites. But Doctor Faustus drank and was full of good cheer, taking his pleasure and dalliance there. When he was through he used the same art as before and ascended into the sky in papish raiment and ornament.

Now when Faustus was gone and the fog disappeared, the Turk came to his castle, summoned his wives and asked who had been there while the castle was for so long surrounded with fog. They informed him how it was the god Mahomet who at night had called this one and that one to him, lain with them and said that from his seed would rise up a great nation and valiant heroes. The Turk accepted it as a great benefit that Mahomet had lain with his wives, but he wondered if it had been accomplished according to the manner of mortals. Oh yes, they answered, that was the way it had been done. He had called them, embraced them, and was well fitted out — they would fain be served in such sort every day. He had lain with them naked and was certainly a man in all parts, except that they had not been able to understand his tongue. The priests instructed the Turk that he ought not believe it were Mahomet, but rather a phantom. The wives on the other hand said, be it ghost or man, he had been very kind to them and had served them masterfully, once or six times — nay, even more often — in a night; all of which caused the Turk much contemplation, and he remained doubtful in the matter.

Concerning the Stars

XIX

A prominent scholar in Halberstadt, Doctor N. V. W., invited Doctor Faustus to his table. Before supper was ready, Faustus stood for a while gazing out the window at the Heavens, it being Harvest time and the sky filled with stars. Now his host, being also a Doctor of Physic and a good *astrologus,* had brought Doctor Faustus here for the purpose of learning from him divers transformations in the planets and stars. Therefore he now leaned upon the window beside Doctor Faustus and looked also upon the brilliance of the Heavens, the multitude of stars, some of which were shooting through the sky and falling to the earth. In all humility he made request that Doctor Faustus might tell him the condition and quality of this thing.

Doctor Faustus began in this wise: My most dear Lord and Brother, this condition doth presuppose certain other matters which ye must understand first. The smallest star in Heaven, although when beheld from below it seems to our thinking scarcely so big as our large wax candles, is really larger than a principality. Oh yes, this is certain. I have seen that the length and breadth of the Heavens is many times greater than the surface of the earth. From Heaven, ye cannot even see earth. Many a star is broader than this land, and most are at least as large as this city. — See, over there is one fully as large as the dominion of the Roman Empire. This one right up here is as large as Turkey. And up higher there, where the planets are, ye may find one as big as the world.

A Question on This Topic

XX

I know that to be true, saith this doctor. But my Lord Faustus, how is it with the spirits who vex men and thwart their works (as some people say) by day and by night as well?

Doctor Faustus answered: We ought not to begin with this topic, but with the ordinances and creation of God, it being in accordance with these that the sun doth at break of day turn again toward the world with his radiance (it being also nearer in summer than in winter), and that the spirits then move beneath the cloud sphere where God hath committed them that they may discover all his portents. As the day progresses, they rise upward beneath the cloud sphere, for they are granted no affinity with the sun: the brighter it shines, the higher they do seek to dwell. In this context we might speak of forbidden days, for God hath not granted them light nor allowed them such a property.

But by night, when it is pitch dark, then they are among us, for the brightness of the sun — even though it is not shining here — is in the first Heaven so intense that it is as daylight there (this being why, in the blackness of night, even when the stars do not shine, men still perceive Heaven). It followeth therefore that the spirits, not being able to endure or to suffer the aspect of the sun, which hath now ascended upwards, must come near to us on earth and dwell with men, frightening them with nightmares, howling and spooks. Now what will ye wager and bet: when ye go abroad in the dark without a light — if ye dare do such a thing — a great fear will seize you. Furthermore, if ye are alone by night ye are possessed by strange phantasies, although the day bringeth no such things. At night some will start up in their sleep, another thinks there be a spirit near him, or that he be groping out for him, or that he walk round in the house, or in his sleep, etc. There are many such trials, all because the spirits are near to vex and plague men with multitudinous delusions.

The Second Question

XXI

I thank you very much, spake the doctor, my dear Lord Faustus, for your brief account. I shall remember it and ponder upon it my life long. But, if I may trouble you further, would ye not instruct me once more as concerns the brilliance of the stars and their appearance by night.

Yea, very briefly, answered Doctor Faustus. Now it is certain that, so soon as the sun doth ascend into the Third Heaven (if it should move down into the First Heaven, it would ignite the earth — but the time for that is not come yet, and the earth must still proceed along her God-ordained course), when the sun doth so far withdraw itself, I say, then doth it become the right of the stars to shine for as long as God hath ordained. The First and Second Heavens, which contain these stars, are then brighter than two of our summer days, and offer an excellent refuge for the birds by night.

Night, therefore, observed from Heaven, is nothing else than day, or, as one might also aver, the day is half the night. For ye must understand that when the sun ascends, leaving us here in night, the day is just beginning in such places as India and Africa. And when our sun shineth, their day waneth, and they have night.

The Third Question

XXII

But I still do not understand, spake the Doctor from Halberstadt, the action of the stars, how they glitter, and how they fall down to earth.

Doctor Faustus answered: This is nothing out of the ordinary, but an every-day happening. It is indeed true that the stars, like the Firmament and other *Elementa,* were created and disposed in the Heavens in such a fashion that they are immutable. But they do have their changes in color and in other external circumstances. The stars are undergoing superficial changes of this sort when they give off sparks or little flames, for these are bits of match falling from the stars — or, as we call them, shooting stars. They are hard, black, and greenish.

But that a star itself might fall — why this is nothing more than a fancy of mankind. When by night a great streak of fire is seen to shoot downward, these are not falling stars, although we do call them that, but only slaggy pieces from the stars. They are big things, to be sure, and, as is true of the stars themselves, some are much bigger than others. But it is my opinion that no star itself falleth except as a scourge of God. Then such falling stars bring a murkiness of the Heavens with them and cause great floods and devastation of lives and land.

HERE FOLLOWETH THE THIRD
PART DOCTOR FAUSTUS HIS
ADVENTURES THE THINGS HE
PERFORMED AND WORKED
WITH HIS *NIGROMANTIA* AT THE
COURTS OF GREAT POTENTATES

A History of the Emperor Charles V and Doctor Faustus

XXIII

Our Emperor Charles the Fifth of that name was come with his court entourage to Innsbruck, whither Doctor Faustus had also resorted. Well acquainted with his arts and skill were divers knights and counts, particularly those whom he had relieved of sundry pains and diseases, so that he was invited, summonsed and accompanied to meat at court. Here the Emperor espied him and wondered who he might be. When someone remarked that it was Doctor Faustus, the Emperor noted it well, but held his peace until after meat (this being in the summer and after St. Philip and St. James). Then the Emperor summoned Faustus into his Privy Chamber and, disclosing to him that he deemed him adept in *nigromantia,* did therefore desire to be shown a proof in something which he would like to know. He vowed unto Faustus by his Imperial Crown that no ill should befall him, and Doctor Faustus did obediently acquiesce to oblige his Imperial Majesty.

Now hear me then, quoth the Emperor. In my camp I once did stand athinking, how my ancestors before me did rise to such high degree and sovereignty as would scarcely be attainable for me and my successors, especially how Alexander the Great, of all monarchs the most mighty, was a light and an ornament among all Emperors. Ah, it is well known what great riches, how many kingdoms and territories he did possess and acquire, the which to conquer and to organize again will fall most difficult for me and my succession, such territories being now divided into many separate kingdoms. It is my constant wish that I had been acquainted with this man and had been able to behold him and his spouse in the person, figure, form, mien and bearing of life. I understand that thou be an adept master in thine art, able to realize all things according to matter and complexion, and my most gracious desire is that thou give me some answer now in this regard.

Most gracious Lord, quoth Faustus, I will, in so far as I with my spirit am able, comply with Your Imperial Majesty's desire as concerns the personages of Alexander and his spouse, their aspect and figure, and cause them to appear here. But Your Majesty shall know that their mortal bodies cannot be present, risen up from the dead, for such is impossible. Rather, it will be after this wise: the spirits are experienced, most wise and ancient spirits, able to assume the bodies of such people, so transforming themselves that Your Imperial Majesty will in this manner behold the veritable Alexander.

Faustus then left the Emperor's chamber to take counsel with his spirit. Being afterward come in again to the Emperor's chamber, he indicated to him that he was about to be obliged, but upon the one condition that he would pose no questions, nor speak at all, the which the Emperor agreed unto. Doctor Faustus opened the door. Presently Emperor Alexander entered in the very form which he had borne in life — namely: a well-proportioned, stout little man with a red or red-blond, thick beard, ruddy cheeks and a countenance as austere as had he the eyes of the Basilisk. He stepped forward in full harness and, going up to Emperor Charles, made a low and reverent curtsey before him. Doctor Faustus restrained the Emperor of Christendom from rising up to receive him. Shortly thereafter, Alexander having again bowed and being gone out at the door, his spouse now approached the Emperor, she, too, making a curtesy. She was

Presently Emperor Alexander entered in the very form he had borne in life

clothed all in blue velvet, embroidered with gold pieces and pearls. She, too, was excellent fair and rosy-cheeked, like unto milk and blood mixed, tall and slender, and with a round face.

Emperor Charles was thinking the while: Now I have seen two personages whom I have long desired to know, and certainly it cannot be otherwise but that the spirit hath indeed changed himself into these forms, and he doth not deceive me, it being even as with the woman who raised the prophet Samuel for Saul.

But desiring to be the more certain of the matter, the Emperor thought to himself: I have often heard tell that she had a great wen on her back. If it is to be found upon this image also, then I would believe it all the better.

So, stepping up to her, he did lift her skirt, and he found the wen. For she stood stock still for him, disappearing again afterwards. Thus the Emperor's desire was granted withal, and he was sufficiently content.

Concerning the Antlers of a Hart

Upon a time soon after Doctor Faustus had accomplished the Emperor's will as was reported above he, hearing the signal for meat in the evening, did lean over the battlements to watch the domestics go out and in. There he espied one who was fallen asleep while lying in the window of the great Knights' Hall across the court (it being very hot). I would not name the person, for it was a knight and a gentleman by birth.

Now with the aid of his spirit Mephostophiles, Faustus did charm a pair of hart's horns upon the knight's head. This good lord's head nodded upon the window sill, he awoke, and per-

The trip to Munich and back

ceived the prank. Who could have been more distressed! For, the windows being closed, he could go neither forward nor backward with his antlers, nor could he force the horns from off his head. The Emperor, observing his plight, laughed and was well pleased withal until Doctor Faustus at last released the poor knight from the spell again.

Concerning Three Lords Who Were Rapidly Transported to the Royal Wedding in Munich

XXV

Three sons of noble lords (whom I dare not call by name) were students in Wittemberg. They met together on a time and, talking of the magnificent pomp which would attend the wedding of the son of the Duke of Bavaria in Munich, did heartily wish that they might go there, if only for a half an hour. Such talk caused the one of them to take thought of Doctor Faustus, and he said to the other two lords:

Cousins, if ye will follow me, hush and keep it to yourselves, then will I give you good counsel, how we can see the wedding and then be back to Wittemberg again in the self-same night. Here is what I have in mind: if we send for Doctor Faustus, tell him what we desire, and explain our plans to him, giving him a bit of money besides, then he surely will not deny us his aid.

Having deliberated and agreed upon the matter, they called on Doctor Faustus, who, touched by their present and also being well pleased with a banquet which they were clever enough to give in his honor, did consent to grant them his services.

The day arrived when the wedding of the Bavarian Duke's

son was to be celebrated, and Doctor Faustus sent word to the young lords that they should come to his house arrayed in the very finest clothing they possessed. He then took a broad cloak, spread it out in his garden (which lay right beside his house), seated the lords upon it, himself in their midst, and at last gave strict command that none should speak a word so long as they be abroad — even though they be in the Bavarian Duke's Palace and someone should speak to them, they should give no answer — the which they all did pledge to obey. This matter being settled, Doctor Faustus sat down and commenced his *coniurationes*. Presently there arose a great wind which lifted the cloak and transported them through the air with such speed that they arrived betimes at the Duke's court in Munich.

They had travelled invisible, so that no one noticed them until they entered the Bavarian Palace and came into the hall, where the Marshall, espying them, indicated to the Duke of Bavaria how, although the princes, lords and gentlemen were already seated at table, there were still standing three more gentlemen without who had just arrived with a servant, and who also ought to be received. The old Duke of Bavaria arose to do this, but when he approached and spake to them, none would utter a word.

This occurred in the evening just before meat, they having hitherto observed all day the pomp of the wedding without any hindrance, for Faustus' art had kept them invisible. As was reported above, Doctor Faustus had sternly forbidden them to speak this day. He had further instructed them that so soon as he should call out: Up and away! all were to seize upon the cloak at once, and they would fly away again in the twinkling of an eye.

Now when the Duke of Bavaria spake to them and they gave no answer, handwater was proffered them anyhow. It was then that Doctor Faustus, hearing one of the lords forget himself and violate his command, did cry aloud: Up and away! Faustus and the two lords who held to the cloak were instantly flown away, but the third, who had been negligent, was taken captive and cast into a cell. The other two lords did upon arrival at midnight in Wittemberg behave so glumly on account of their kinsman that Doctor Faustus sought to console them, and he promised that the young man would be released by morning.

The captive lord, being thus forsaken, in locked custody besides, and constrained by guards, was sore afraid. To make matters worse, he was questioned as to what manner of vision he had been a part of, and as to the other three who were now vanished away.

He thought: If I betray them, then the ending will be bad.

He therefore gave answer to none who were sent to him, and when they saw that nothing was to be got out of him this day they finally informed him that on the morrow he would be brought down to the dungeon, tortured, and compelled to speak. The lord thought to himself:

So my ordeal is appointed for the morrow. If Doctor Faustus should not release me today, should I be tortured and racked, well then I needs must speak.

But he still had the consolation that his friends would entreat Doctor Faustus for his release, and that is indeed the way it fell out. Before day break Doctor Faustus was in the cell, having cast such a spell on the watch that they fell into a heavy sleep. Faustus used his art to open all doors and locks, and he brought the lord punctually to Wittemberg, where a sumptuous honorarium was presented him as a reward.

Concerning an Adventure with a Jew

XXVI

It is said that the fiend and the sorcerer will not wax three penny richer in a year, and even so did it come to pass with Doctor Faustus. Much had been promised by his spirit, but much had been lies, for the Devil is the spirit of lies. Mephostophiles had once reproached Doctor Faustus, saying:

With the skill wherewith I have endowed thee thou shouldst acquire thine own wealth. Such arts as mine and thine can scarcely lose thee money. Thy years are not yet over. Only four years are past since my promise to thee that thou wouldst want neither for gold nor for goods. Why, thy meat and drink hath been brought thee from the courts of all the great potentates, all by mine art (what the spirit here states, we did already report above).

Doctor Faustus, who did not know how to disagree with these things, began to take thought and to wonder just how apt he might be in obtaining money. Not long after the spirit had told him those things, Faustus went banqueting with some good fellows and, finding himself without money, went and raised some in the Jewish quarter, accepting sixty Talers for a month's time.

The money-lender, when the loan fell due, was ready to take his capital together with the usury, but Doctor Faustus was not at all of the opinion that he ought to pay anything. The fellow

From my body I will amputate a member

appeared at Faustus' house with his demand and received this answer:

Jew, I have no money. I can raise no money. But this I will do. From my body I will amputate a member, be it arm or leg, and give it thee in pawn — but it must be returned so soon as I am in money again.

The Jew (for Jews are enemies to us Christians, anyhow) pondered the matter and concluded that it must be a right reckless man who would place his limbs in pawn. But still he accepted it. Doctor Faustus took a saw and, cutting off his leg withal, committed it unto the Jew (but it was only a hoax) upon the condition that it must be returned so soon as he be in money again and would pay his debt, for he would fain put the member back on. The Jew went away with the leg, well satisfied at first with his contract and agreement. But very soon he became vexed and tired of the leg, for he thought:

What good to me is a knave's leg? If I carry it home it will begin to stink. I doubt that he will be able to put it on again whole, and, besides, this pledge is a parlous thing for me, for no higher pawn can a man give than his own limb. But what profit will I have of it?

Thinking these and such like things as he crossed over a bridge, the Jew did cast the leg into the water. Doctor Faustus knew all about this of course, and three days later he summoned the Jew in order to pay and settle his account. The Jew appeared and explained his considerations, saying he had thrown the leg away because it was of no use to anyone. Doctor Faustus immediately demanded that his pledge be returned or that some other settlement be made. The Jew was eager to be free of Faustus, and he finally had to pay him sixty Guilders more (Doctor Faustus still having his leg as before).

An Adventure at the Court
of the Count of Anhalt

XXVII

Doctor Faustus came upon a time to the Count of Anhalt, where he was received with all kindness and graciousness. Now this was in January, and at table he perceived that the Countess was great with child. When the evening meat had been carried away and the collation of sweets was being served, Doctor Faustus said to the Countess:

Gracious Lady, I have always heard that the greatbellied women long for diverse things to eat. I beg your Grace not to conceal from me what you would please to have.

She answered him: Truly my Lord, I will not conceal from you my present wish that it were Harvest time, and I were able to eat my fill of fresh grapes and of other fruit.

Hereupon Doctor Faustus said: Gracious Lady, this is easy for me to provide. In an hour your Grace's will shall be accomplished.

Doctor Faustus now took two silver bowls and set them out before the window. When the hour was expired he reached out the window and drew in one bowl with white and red grapes which were fresh from the vine, and the other bowl full of green apples and pears, but all of a strange and exotic sort. Placing them before the Countess, he said to her:

Your Grace need have no fear to eat, for I tell you truly that they are from a foreign nation where summer is about to end, although our year is, to be sure, just beginning here.

While the Countess did eat of all the fruit with pleasure and great wonderment, the Count of Anhalt could not withhold to ask for particulars concerning the grapes and other fruit.

Doctor Faustus answered: Gracious Lord, may it please your Grace to know that the year is divided into two circles in the world, so that it is summer in Orient and Occident when it is winter here, for the Heavens are round. Now, from where we dwell the sun hath now withdrawn to the highest point, so that we are having short days and winter here, but at the same time it is descending upon Orient and Occident — as in Sheba, India and in the East proper. The meaning of this is that they are having summer now. They enjoy vegetables and fruit twice a year there. Furthermore, gracious Lord, when it is night here, day is just dawning there. The sun hath even now betaken himself beneath the earth, and it is night; but in this same instant the sun doth run above the earth there, and they shall have day (in likeness thereof, the sea runneth higher than the world, and if it were not obedient to God, it could inundate the world in a moment). In consideration of such knowledge, gracious Lord, I sent my spirit to that nation upon the circumference of the sea where the sun now riseth, although it setteth here. He is a flying spirit and swift, able to transform himself in the twinkling of an eye. He hath procured these grapes and fruit for us.

The Count did attend these revelations with great wonderment.

The Manner in Which Doctor Faustus
as *Bacchus* Kept Shrovetide

XXVIII

The greatest effort, skill and art produced by Doctor Faustus was that which he demonstrated to the Count of Anhalt, for with the aid of his spirit he accomplished not merely the things I have told about, but he created all sorts of four-footed beasts as well as winged and feathered fowl, too. Now after he had taken leave of the Count and was returned back to Wittemberg, Shrovetide approached. Doctor Faustus himself played the role of *Bacchus*, entertaining several learned students, whom he persuaded (after they had been well fed and sated by Faustus, had crowned him *Bacchus* and were in the act of celebrating him) to go into a cellar with him and to try the magnificent drinks which he would there offer and provide them, a thing to which they readily assented. Doctor Faustus then laid out a ladder in his garden, seated a man on each rung, and away he whisked, coming by night into the cellar of the Bishop of Saltzburg.

Here they tasted all sorts of wine, for this bishop hath a glorious grape culture, but when the good gentlemen were just in a fine temper, the Bishop's butler by chance did come downstairs and, seeing them (for Doctor Faustus had brought along a flint so that they might better inspect all the casks), did charge them as thieves who had broken in. This offended Doctor Faustus, who, warning his fellows to prepare to leave, seized the butler by the

Here they tasted all sorts of wine

hair and rode away with him until he saw a great high fir tree, in the top of which he deposited the frightened man. Being returned home again, he and his Shrovetide guests celebrated a *valete* with the wine which he had brought along in a big bottle from the Bishop's cellar.

The poor butler had to hold fast all night to the tree, lest he fall out, and he almost froze to death. When day brake and he perceived the great height of the fir as well as the impossibility of climbing down (for it had no branches except in the very top), he had to call out to some peasants whom he saw drive by, and tell them what had happened to him. The peasants did marvel at all this and, coming into Saltzburg, reported it at court. This brought out a great crowd, who with much exertion and effort with ropes did bring the butler down. But he never knew who those were whom he had found in the cellar, nor who he was who had put him into the tree top.

Concerning Helen, Charmed Out of Greece

XXIX

On Whitsunday the students came unannounced to Doctor Faustus' residence for dinner, but, as they brought ample meat and drink along, they were welcome guests. The wine was soon going round at table, and they fell to talking of beautiful women, one of the students asserting that there were no woman whom he would rather see than fair Helen from Greece, for whose sake the worthy city of Troy had perished. She must have been beautiful, he said, for she had been stolen away from her husband, and a great deal of strife had arisen on her account.

Doctor Faustus said: Inasmuch as ye are so eager to behold the beautiful figure of Queen Helen, I have provided for her awakening and will now conduct her hither so that ye may see her spirit for yourselves, just as she appeared in life (in the same way, after all, that I granted Emperor Charles V his wish to see the person of Emperor Alexander the Great and his spouse).

Forbidding that any should speak or arise from table to receive her, Faustus went out of the parlor and, coming in again, was followed at the heel by Queen Helen, who was so wondrously beautiful that the students did not know whether they were still in their right minds, so confused and impassioned were they become. For she appeared in a precious deep purple robe, her hair, which shone golden and quite beautifully glorious, hanging down to her knees. She had coal black eyes, a sweet countenance on a round little head. Her lips were red as the red cherries, her mouth small, and her neck like a white swan's. She had cheeks pink like a rose, an exceeding fair and smooth complexion and a rather slim, tall and erect bearing. *In summa,* there was not a flaw about her to be criticized. Helen looked all around in the parlor with a right wanton mien, so that the students were violently inflamed with love for her, but since they took her to be a spirit they controlled their passion without difficulty, and she

Helen looked all around in the parlor with a right wanton mien

left the room again with Doctor Faustus.

After the vision had passed away, the young men begged Faustus to be so good as to have the image appear just once more, for they would fain send a painter to his house the next day to make a counterfeit of her. This Doctor Faustus refused to do, saying that he could not make her spirit appear at just any time, but that he would procure such a portrait for them. Later, he did indeed produce one, and all the students had it copied by sending painters to his house (for it was a fair and glorious figure of a woman). Now it is unknown to this day who got this painting away from Doctor Faustus.

As concerns the students, when they came to bed they could not sleep for thinking of the figure and form which had appeared visibly before them, and from this we may learn how the Devil doth blind men with love — oh it doth often happen that a man goeth awhoring for so long that at last he can no longer be saved from it.

Concerning a Gesticulation
Involving Four Wheels

XXX

Doctor Faustus was summoned and commanded to come to the town of Brunswick to cure a marshall there who had consumption. Now he used to ride neither horseback nor by coach, but was of a mind to walk wherever he was invited as a guest or summoned as a physician. When he was about a half a quarter from Brunswick and could see the town before him, a peasant with four horses and an empty wagon came clattering along. Doctor Faustus addressed the clown in all kindness, requesting that he be allowed to climb on and be driven the rest of the way up to the town gate, but the bumpkin refused to do this and turned Faustus away, saying he would have enough to haul on his return trip. Doctor Faustus had not been serious in his request, wanting only to prove the peasant, whether there were any love to be found in him, but now he repaid the clown's churlishness (such as is, after all, commonly found among peasants) in like coin, speaking to him thus:

Thou bumpkin and worthless ass, since thou hast demonstrated such churlishness unto me, and since thou wilt certainly use others the same and probably already hast done so, thou shalt this time be paid for thy trouble. Thy four wheels shalt thou find one at each gate of Brunswick town.

Immediately the wagon wheels sprang away, floating along in the air so that each one came to a different gate, without being

Immediately the wagon wheels sprang away

noticed by anyone there. The peasant's horses also fell down as if they had suddenly died and lay there quite still. At this was the poor clown sore affright, measuring it as a special scourge of God for his misanthropy. All troubled and weeping, with outstretched hands and upon his knees, he did beg Faustus for forgiveness, confessing himself indeed well worthy of such punishment, but vowing that the next time this would serve as a remembrance to him, so that he would never use such misanthropy again.

Doctor Faustus took pity upon the clown's humility and answered him, saying that he must treat no one else in this hard manner, there being nothing more shameful than the qualities of churlishness and misanthropy — and the wicked pride which accompanieth them. Now the man should but take up some earth and throw it upon the team, which would then rise up and live out its days. So it came to pass, Faustus saying as he departed from the peasant:

Thy churlishness cannot go altogether unpunished, but must be repaid in equal measure, inasmuch as thou hast deemed it such a great effort to take a tired man onto an empty wagon. Lo, thy wheels are without the town at four different gates. There wilt thou find all four of them.

The peasant went along and found them as Doctor Faustus had said, but with great effort, travail and neglect of the trade and business which he had intended to accomplish. And thus will churlishness ever punish its owner.

Concerning Four Sorcerers Who Cut Off One Another's Heads and Put Them On Again, Wherein Doctor Faustus, Attending Their Performance, Doth Play the Major Role

XXXI

Doctor Faustus came to the Carnival in Frankfurt, where his spirit Mephostophiles did inform him that there were four sorcerers at an inn in Jews Alley who were attracting a great audience by chopping off one another's heads and sending them to the barber to be trimmed. Now that vexed Faustus, who liked to think that he were the only cock in the Devil's basket. When he went to behold the thing, he found the sorcerers just getting ready to chop off their heads, and with them was a barber who was going to trim and wash them. Upon a table they had a glass cruse with distilled water in it. One among them, the chief sorcerer and also their executioner, laid his hands upon the first of his fellows and charmed a lily into this cruse. It waxed green, and he called it the Root of Life. Now he beheaded that first fellow, let the barber dress the head, then set it upon the man's shoulders again. In one and the same instant, the lily disappeared and the man was whole again. This was done with the second and the third sorcerer in like manner. A lily was charmed for each in the water, they were executed, their heads were then dressed and put back on them again.

He called it the Root of Life

At last it was the turn of the chief sorcerer and executioner. His Root of Life was blooming away in the water and waxing green, now his head was smitten off also, and they set to washing it and dressing it in Faustus' presence, which sorcery did sorely vex him: the arrogance of this *magicus princeps,* how he let his head be chopped off so insolently, with blasphemy and laughter in his mouth. Doctor Faustus went up to the table where the cruse and the flowering lily stood, took out his knife, and snipped the flower, severing the stem. No one was aware of this at the time, but when the sorcerers sought to set the head on again their medium was gone, and the evil fellow had to perish with his sins upon his severed head.

Afterwards they did find the stem cut, but they were not able to discover how this came to pass. This is the way the Devil at last rewards all his servants, absolving them thus, the manner in which Doctor Faustus dealt with this man being entirely consonant with the shameful absolution which he did himself receive when he was repaid for his own sins.

Concerning an Old Man Who Would
Have Converted Doctor Faustus
from His Godless Life

XXXII

A Christian, pious, godfearing physician, a person zealous of the honor of God, was also a neighbor of Doctor Faustus, and, seeing that many students frequented Faustus' house, he considered such a den as bad as a brothel, for he did compare Faustus to all the Jews, who, so soon as they fell away from God also became His declared enemies, dedicating themselves unto sorcery for the sake of prophecy and deceit, seeking not only the bodily harm of many a pious child whose parents have devoted much effort to his Christian rearing, but also causing him to forget the Lord's Prayer. This old neighbor of Doctor Faustus had observed his rascality in such a light for long years and no longer doubted the devilish nature of his mischief, but he also knew that the time was not yet ripe for the civil authorities to establish these facts.

Considering thus above all the weal of the young men he did in Christian zeal summon Faustus as a guest into his own lodging. Faustus came, and at table his old godfearing patron addressed him thus:

My sweet Lord, as a friend and as a Christian I ask you not to receive my discourse in rancor and in ill will, nor to despise these small victuals, but charitably to take and to be content with what our sweet Lord provideth us.

Doctor Faustus requested him to declare his purpose, saying he would attend him obediently. His patron then commenced:

My sweet Lord and Neighbor, ye know your own actions, that ye have defied God and all the Saints, that ye have given yourself up unto the Devil, whereby ye are now come into God's greatest wrath and are changed from a Christian into a very heretic and devil. O why do ye deprave your soul! Ye must not heed the body, but your sweet soul, lest ye reside in the eternal punishment and displeasure of God. Look ye to it, my Lord, ye are not yet lost if ye will but turn from your evil way, beseech God for Grace and pardon, as ye may see in the example in *Acts* VIII concerning Simon in Samaria, who had also traduced many. They thought him to be a god, calling him the Power of God and *Simon Deus Sanctus*. But he was converted when he heard a sermon of St. Philip, was baptized and did believe on our Lord Jesus Christ. It is particularly noted and praised in *Acts* how he did afterward much consort with Philip. Thus, my Lord, allow my sermon also to appeal to you. O, let it be a heartfelt Christian admonition! To sin no more is the penance wherewith ye must seek Grace and pardon, as ye may learn from the fine examples of the thief on the cross, as well as from St. Peter, St. Matthew and Magdalena. Yea, Christ our Lord speaketh unto all sinners: Come unto me, all ye that labor and are heavy laden, and I will give you rest. Or, in the Prophet Ezekiel: I have no pleasure in the death of the wicked; but that the wicked should turn from his way and live, for his hand is not withered, that he were no longer useful. I beg you my Lord, take my plea to your heart, ask God for pardon for Christ's sake, and abjure at the same time your evil practices, for sorcery is against God and His Commandment, inasmuch as He doth sorely forbid it in both the Old and the New Testaments. He speaketh: Ye shall not allow them to live, ye shall not seek after them nor hold counsel with them, for it is an abomination unto God. Thus St. Paul called Bar-Jesus, or Elymas the Sorcerer, a child of the Devil and an enemy of all righteousness, saying that such should have no share in the Kingdom of God.

Doctor Faustus attended him diligently and said that the speech had well pleased him. He expressed his gratitude to the old man for his good will and took his leave, promising to comply in so far as he was able.

When he arrived home he took the old man's counsel to heart, considering how he had indeed depraved his soul by yielding himself up to the accursed Devil, and at last Faustus felt a desire to do penance and to revoke his promise to the Devil.

What is thy purpose with thyself?

While he was occupied in such thoughts, his spirit appeared unto him, groping after him as if to twist his head off his shoulders. The spirit then spake, rebuking him:

What is thy purpose with thyself?

He reminded him of his motives in first consigning himself to the Devil. Having promised enmity toward God and all mankind, he was not now fulfilling that pledge but was following after this old reprobate, feeling charity toward a man and hence

103

toward God — now, when it was already too late and when he was clearly the property of the Devil.

The Devil hath the power (he spake) to fetch thee away. I am in fact now come with the command to dispose of thee — or to obtain thy promise that thou wilt never more allow thyself to be seduced, and that thou wilt consign thyself anew with thy blood. Thou must declare immediately what thou wouldst do, or I am to slay thee.

Sore affright, Doctor Faustus consented, sat down and with his blood did write as followeth (this document being found after his death):

Pact

XXXIII

I, Doctor Johann Faustus,

Do declare in this mine own hand and blood:

Whereas I have truly and strictly observed my first *instrumentum* and pact for these nineteen years, in defiance of God and all mankind;

And whereas, pledging body and soul, I therein did empower the mighty God Lucifer with full authority over me so soon as five more years be past;

And whereas he hath further promised me to increase my days in death, thereby shortening my days in Hell, also not to allow me to suffer any pain;

Now therefore do I further promise him that I will never more heed the admonitions, teachings, scoldings, instructions or threats of mankind, neither as concerneth the Word of God nor in any temporal or spiritual matters whatsoever; but particularly do I promise to heed no man of the cloth nor to follow his teachings.

In good faith and resolve contracted by these presents and in mine own blood, etc.

Now just as soon as Faustus had executed this godless, damned pact, he began to hate the good old man so intensely that he sought some means to kill him, but the old man's Christian prayers and Christian ways did such great offense to the Evil Fiend that he could not even approach him.

Two days after the events just recounted, when the old man was retiring, he heard a mighty rumbling in his house, the like of which he was never wont to hear. It came right into his chamber, grunting like a sow and continuing for a long time. Lying abed, the old man began to mock the spirit, saying:

Ah, what a fine bawdy music! Now what a beautiful hymn sung by a ghoul! Really a pretty anthem sung by a beautiful angel — who could not tarry in Paradise for two full days. This wretched fellow must now go avisiting in other folks' houses, for he is banished from his own home.

With such mockery he drave the spirit away. When Doctor Faustus asked him how he had fared with the old man, Mephostophiles answered that he had not been able to lay hold on him, for he had worn armor (referring to the prayers of the old man) and had mocked him besides.

Now the spirits and devils cannot suffer a good humor, particularly when they are reminded of their fall. Thus doth God protect all good Christians who seek in Him succor against the Evil One.

DOCTOR FAUSTUS HIS LAST
TRICKS AND WHAT HE DID
IN THE FINAL YEARS
OF HIS CONTRACT

How Doctor Faustus Brought About
the Marriage of Two Lovers

XXXIV

A student in Wittemberg, a gallant gentleman of the nobility named N. Reuckauer, was with heart and eyes far gone in love with an equally noble and exceedingly beautiful gentlewoman. Of the many suitors (among them even a young knight) whom she turned down, this Reuckauer was privileged to occupy the least place of all. But he was a good friend of Doctor Faustus, having often sat with him at meat and at drink, so that when the acute affects of his love for the gentlewoman caused him to pine away and fall ill, Faustus soon learned of it. He asked his spirit Mephostophiles about the cause of this serious condition and, being told that it was the love affair, soon paid a visit to the nobleman, who was greatly astonished to learn the true nature of his illness. Doctor Faustus bade him be of good cheer and not to despair so, for he intended to help him win the affections of this lady so completely that she should never love another. And so it did indeed come to pass, for Doctor Faustus so disturbed the heart of the maiden with his sorcery that she would look upon no other man, nor heed any other suitor, although many gallant, wealthy noblemen were courting her.

Soon after his conversation with Reuckauer, Faustus commanded the young man to clothe himself sumptuously and prepare to accompany him to the maiden's house, for she was

For she was now in her garden

now in her garden with many other guests who were about to begin a dance, and there Reuckauer was to dance with her. Doctor Faustus gave him a ring, telling him to wear it on his finger during the dance with this lady, for just as soon as he might touch her with his ring finger she would fall in love with him and with no other. Faustus forbade Reuckauer to ask her hand in marriage, explaining that she would have to entreat him.

Now he took some distilled water and washed Reuckauer with it, so that his face presently became exceeding handsome. Reuckauer followed Faustus' instructions carefully, danced with the lady and, while dancing, touched her with his ring finger. Instantly, her whole heart and love were his, for the good maiden was pierced through with Cupid's arrow.

That night in her bed she found no rest, so often did her

thoughts turn to Reuckauer. Early the next morning she sent for him, laid her heart and her love before him, and begged him to wed her. He gave his consent, for he loved her ardently. Their wedding was celebrated anon, and Doctor Faustus received a handsome honorarium.

Concerning Divers Flora
in Doctor Faustus' Garden
on Christmas Day

XXXV

In the midst of winter at the Christmas season, several gentle-women came to Wittemberg to visit their brothers and cousins, all young gentlemen students there who were well-acquainted with Doctor Faustus. He had been invited to their table on more than one occasion, and, desirous now of repaying such social debts, he did invite these lords to bring their ladies to his domicile for an evening draught of wine. To come

Beautiful vines were growing there

to his house, they had to trudge through a deep snow which lay over the town, but Doctor Faustus had used his peculiar sorcery to prepare a splendid marvel in his garden for them, and when they arrived there they beheld no snow at all, but a lovely summer day with all manner of flora. The grass was covered all over with many blossoms. Beautiful vines were growing there, all hung with divers sorts of grapes. There were roses, too, white, red and pink, as well as many other sweet-smelling flowers, and it was all a great delight to behold.

Concerning an Army Raised Against
My Lord of Hardeck

XXXVI

Doctor Faustus, being on a journey to Eisleben and about halfway there, did see seven horse riding in the distance. He recognized their leader, for it was that Lord of Hardeck upon whose forehead (as we have reported) he had charmed a set of hart's horns while at the Emperor's court. The lord, who knew Faustus quite as well as Faustus knew him, called his men to a halt, and when Faustus noticed this action he immediately retired toward a little hill.

The knight ordered a lively charge to intercept him, and also commanded the firing of a musket volley, but although they spurred their mounts hard to overtake Faustus, he achieved the higher ground first, and by the time the horses had topped the rise he had vanished from their sight. Here the knight called a halt. They were looking about, trying to catch sight of Faustus again, when they heard in the copse below a loud noise of horns, trumpets and military drums, all tooting and beating. Some hundred horse came charging in upon them, and the knight with his men took to their heels.

They at first sought to slip around the side of the hill home, but they encountered a second great armed band all ready for the charge and barring their way. They turned about to dash away and beheld a third troop of horsemen. They tried still another route, but again found themselves faced with men ready for battle. The same thing happend five times, just as often as they turned in a fresh direction. When the knight saw that he could nowhere escape but was threatened with a charge from every direction, he rode alone right into the main host, ignoring the danger to himself, and asked what might be the cause for his being surrounded and menaced on all quarters.

None would speak to him or say a word until at last Doctor Faustus came riding up to the knight (who was now restrained on all sides) and proposed that he surrender himself as a prisoner or taste the edge of the sword. The knight was convinced that he had encountered a natural army prepared for battle, and when Faustus now demanded their muskets and swords, then took their horses as well, it did not occur to him that it might be naught but sorcery. Presently, Doctor Faustus brought the men fresh, enchanted horses and new muskets and swords, saying to the knight (who no longer even knew him to be Faustus):

My Lord, the commander of this army hath bid me let you go this time — but upon a condition and probation. Will ye confess that ye did pursue a man who hath sought and received, and is henceforth shielded by, our commander's protection?

The knight had to accept this condition. When they came back to his castle again, his men rode the horses out to drink, but once in the water the horses disappeared. The good fellows almost drowned, and had to ride back home afoot. When the knight beheld his men coming in all muddy and wet, and when he learned the cause of it all, he knew right away that it was Doctor Faustus' sorcery, even of the same sort as had been used to shame and mock him before. But since he had this time given Faustus his pledge, he would not break it. As for Faustus, he hitched the horses together, sold them and got some money in his pockets again. Thus did he heap coals upon the wrath of his enemy.

Concerning the Beautiful Helen
from Greece, How She Lived for a Time
with Doctor Faustus

XXXVII

Doctor Faustus would fain omit or neglect naught pleasant and good unto the flesh. One midnight towards the end of the twenty-second year of his pact, while lying awake, he took thought again of Helen of Greece, whom he had awakened for the students on Whitsunday in Shrovetide (which we reported). Therefore, when morning came, he informed his spirit that he must present Helen to him, so that she might be his concubine.

This was done, and Helen was of the following description (Doctor Faustus had a portrait made of her): Her body was fine and erect, well-proportioned, tall, snow-white and crystalline. She had a complexion which seemed tinted with rose, a laughing demeanor, gold-yellow hair which reached almost to the calves of her legs, and brilliant laughing eyes with a sweet, loving gaze. Her nose was somewhat long, her teeth white as alabaster. *In summa*, there was not a single flaw about her body. Doctor Faustus beheld her and she captured his heart. He fell to frolicking with her, she became his bedfellow, and he came to love her so well that he could scarcely bear a moment apart from her.

While fond Faustus was living with Helen, she swelled up as

were she with child. Doctor Faustus was rapturously happy, for, in the twenty-third year of his pact, she bare him a son whom he called Justus Faustus. This child told him many

He fell to frolicking with her, she became his bedfellow

things out of the future history of numerous lands. Later, when Faustus lost his life, there was none who knew whither wife and child were gone.

Concerning One Whose Wife Married While He Was Captive in Turkey, and How Doctor Faustus Informed and Aided Him

XXXVIII

A fine gentleman of the nobility, Johann Werner of Reutt-pueffel from Bennlingen, who had gone to school with Faustus and was a learned man, had been married for six years to an extremely beautiful woman, Sabina of Kettheim, when he was one evening through guile and drink brought to take an oath to go along to Turkey and the Holy Land. He kept his pledge and promise, saw many things, endured much, and had been gone almost five years when there came to his wife certain report that he was dead. The lady mourned for three years, during which time she had many suitors, among them an excellent person of the nobility whose name we dare not mention, but whom she now accepted.

When the time was approaching for their marriage celebration, Doctor Faustus discovered it, and he asked his Mephosto-philes whether this Lord of Reuttpueffel were still alive. The spirit answered yes, he be alive and in Egypt in the city of Lylopolts where he lay captive, having attempted to visit the city of Al-Cairo. This grieved Doctor Faustus, for he loved his friend and had not been pleased that the lady was remarrying so soon. He knew her husband had loved her well. The time for the marriage consummation and the subsequent ceremony being at hand, Doctor Faustus gazed into a mirror wherein he could see all things and by which means he was also able to inform the Lord of Reuttpueffel that his wife was about to be wed, at which the latter was much astonished.

The hour of consummation arrived. The nobleman disrobed and went out to cast his water. It was then that Mephostophiles did use his art, for when the man came in and leapt into Sabina's bed to enjoy the fruits of love, when they hoisted their shirts and squeezed close together, it was all to no avail. The good lady, seeing that he did not want on and was hesitating, did reach out herself for the tool, wishing to help him, but she could achieve naught, and the night wore on in mere grasping, wiggling, and squeezing. This did cause the lady to grieve and to think on her previous husband whom she thought to be dead, for he had rightly known how to tousle her.

On the very same night, Faustus had freed the nobleman and had brought him asleep back to his castle. Now when the good lady beheld her young lord she fell at his feet and begged his forgiveness, indicating at the same time that the other had had naught and had been able to accomplish naught. My Lord of Reuttpueffel, noting that her account corresponded with what Doctor Faustus had reported, did accept her back again. The other good fellow, who finally recovered his potency, rode hastily away, not wishing to be seen again because of what had happened to him. Later, he lost his life in a war. The husband, however, is still jealous, and the good lady must hear from him, even though he did not witness it, how she did after all lie with another, who felt her and grasped her and, had he been able to cover her, would have done that, too.

Concerning the Testament:
What Doctor Faustus Bequeathed
His Servant Christoph Wagner

XXXIX

Now during this whole time, right into the twenty-fourth year of his pact, Doctor Faustus had been keeping a young apprentice, who studied there at the University in Wittemberg and who became acquainted with all the tricks, sorcery and arts of his master. The two were cut from the same piece of cloth. Wagner was a wicked, dissipated knave who had gone about begging in Wittemberg but had found no kindness with anyone until he had met Faustus, who took the stripling in as his famulus and even called him his son, letting him enjoy his ill-gotten gains. Neither troubled himself with the price of them.

When his twenty-four years were all but run out, Faustus called unto himself a notary together with several magisters who were his friends. In their presence he bequeathed his famulus his house and garden, which were located on the Ring-Wall in Scherr Alley, not far from the Iron Gate and indeed right beside the houses of Ganser and of Veitt Röttinger (since that time, it has been rebuilt, for it was so uncanny that none could dwell therein). He also left him 1,600 guilders lent out on usury, a farm worth 800 guilders, 600 guilders in ready money, a gold chain worth 300 crowns, some silver plate given him by a man named Kraffter, as well as such other things as he had taken away from various courts — those of the Pope and of the Turk, for example. All these items together were worth

The two were cut from the same piece of cloth

many hundred guilders. There was not really much household stuff on hand, for he had not lived much at home, but at inns and with students, in gluttony and drunkenness.

The Discourse Which Doctor Faustus Held with His Son Concerning the Testament

XL

The testament being drawn up, Faustus summoned his famulus, explained to him how he had made that person beneficiary of his estate who had been a trusty servant throughout his life and had never revealed any of his secrets, and how he would, in addition, like to grant this person one further request, if he would but name it. Wagner asked for Faust's cunning, but this fine father reminded his pretty son (who should have been named Christ*less* Wagner) that he would after all inherit all his books, and that he must diligently guard them, not letting them become common knowledge, but taking his own profit from them by studying them well (this route to Hell).

As to my cunning (spake Faustus), thou canst win it if thou wilt but love my books, heed no man else, and follow in my footsteps. Hast thou none other request? — That thou be served by my spirit? This cannot be, for Mephostophiles oweth me no further debt, nor doth he bear affinity to any other man. But if thou art fain to have a spirit as servant I will help thee to another.

Three days later, Faustus again called his famulus unto him, asking whether he were still of a mind to possess a spirit, and, if so, in what form he would have him.

In the form of an ape let him appear

My Lord and Father, answered Wagner, in the form of an ape let him appear, for even in such a manner and form would I have him.

A spirit immediately came bounding into the parlor in the figure of an ape, and Doctor Faustus said:

Lo, now seest thou him, but he will not obey thee until I be dead. At that time my Mephostophiles will vanish forever, and thou shalt never see him more. Then, if thou wilt perform what is necessary — this being thine own decision — then canst thou summon thy spirit unto thee by calling upon Urian, for this is his name. In return, I do beg of thee not to publish my deeds, arts and adventures before the time of my death, but then to write all these matters down, organizing and transferring them into a *Historia* and compelling Urian to help thee by recalling unto thee whatever thou canst not remember, for men will expect these things of thee.

What Doctor Faustus Did
in the Final Month of His Pact

XLI

Doctor Faustus became fainthearted, depressed,
deeply melancholic

His days ran out like the sand in an hourglass, and when
only one month remained of the twenty-four years which he
had contracted of the Devil (as ye have read) Doctor Faustus
became fainthearted, depressed, deeply melancholic, like unto
an imprisoned murderer and highwayman over whose head the
sentence hath been pronounced and who now in the dungeon
awaiteth punishment and death. Filled with fear, he sobbed
and held conversations with himself, accompanying such speeches
with many gestures of his hands. He did moan and sigh and
fall away from flesh. He kept himself close and could not abide
to have the spirit about him.

Doctor Faustus His Lamentation, that He Must Die at a Young and a Lusty Age

XLII

Sorrow moved Doctor Faustus to set his grief in words, lest he forget it. Here followeth one such written complaint:

Alas, thou reckless, worthless heart! Thou hast seduced the flesh round about thee, and my fate is fire. The blessedness which once thou didst know is lost.

Alas, Reason and Free Will! What a heavy charge ye do level at these limbs, which may expect naught else than rape of their life!

Alas ye limbs, and thou yet whole body! It was ye let Reason indict Soul, for I might have chosen succor for my soul by sacrificing thee, my body.

Alas, Love and Hate! Why abide ye both at once in my breast? Your company hath occasioned all mine anguish.

Alas, Mercy and Vengeance! Ye have caused me to strive after glory and rewarded me with infamy.

Alas, Malice and Compassion! Was I created a man that I might suffer those torments which now I see before me?

Alas, alas, is there aught in the wide world that doth not conspire against this wretch?

Alas, of what help is this complaint?

Doctor Faustus Lamenteth Yet Further

XLIII

Alas, alas, wretched man, o thou poor accursed Faustus, now in the number of the damned! I must wait the inestimable pains of a death far more miserable than any tortured creature hath yet endured.

Alas, alas, Reason, Willfulness, Recklessness, Free Will! O, what a cursed and inconstant life hast thou led! How unseeing, how careless wast thou! Now become thy parts, soul and body, unseeing and ever more unseen.

Alas, Worldy Pleasure! Into what wretchedness hast thou led me, darkening and blinding mine eyes!

Alas, my timid heart! Where were thine eyes?

And thou my poor soul! Where was thy knowledge?

All ye senses! Where were ye hid?

O miserable travail! O sorrow and desperation forgotten of God!

Alas, grief over grief, and torment upon woe and affliction! Who will release me? Where am I to hide? Whither must I creep? Whither flee? Wherever I may be, there am I a prisoner.

The heart of Doctor Faustus was so troubled that he could speak no more.

Doctor Faustus His Hideous End
and *Spectaculum*

XLIV

His twenty-four years were run out. As he lay awake in the night, his spirit came unto him to deliver up his writ, or contract, thus giving him due notice that the Devil would fetch his body in the following night, and allowing him to make any necessary preparations for that event. This occasioned such a renewed moaning and sobbing into the night that the spirit returned, consoling him and saying:

My Fauste, be not so faint of heart. Thou dost indeed lose thy body, but thy time of judgement is yet far distant. Why surely thou must die — even shouldst thou live for many hundreds of years. The Jews and the Turks must also die expecting the same perdition as thou — even emperors die thus, if they be not Christian. After all, thou knowest not yet what it be that awaiteth thee. Take courage, and despair not so utterly. Dost not remember how the Devil did promise thee a body and soul all of steel, insensitive to the pain which the others will feel in Hell?

This and such like comfort and consolation he gave him, but it was false and not in accord with the Holy Scriptures. Doctor

Faustus, having none other expectation but that he must absolve his debt and contract with his skin, did on this same day (in which the spirit had announced that the Devil was about to fetch him) betake himself unto the trusted friends with whom he

My Fauste, be not so faint of heart

had spent many an hour, the magisters, baccalaureates and other students, entreating them now to go out to the little village of Rimlich with him, about a half mile removed from the town of Wittemberg, there to take a repast with him. They would not turn him away, but went along and ate a morning meal with many costly courses both of meat and of drink, served by the host at an inn.

Doctor Faustus joined in their merriment, but he was not merry in his heart. Afterward, he requested all his guests to do him the great kindness of remaining to eat supper with him, too, and to stay the night here as well, for he had something important to tell them. Again they agreed, and they took the evening meal with him also.

It was finished, and a last cup had been passed. Doctor Faustus paid the host, and addressed the students, saying that he wished to inform them of some things. They gave him their attention, and Doctor Faustus said unto them:

My dear, trusted, and very gracious Lords: I have called you unto me for this good and sufficient cause. For many years now, ye have known what manner of man I be, the arts and the sorcery I have used. All these things come from none other than from the Devil. I fell into such devilish desires through none other cause than these: bad company, mine own worthless flesh and blood, my stiff-necked, godless will, and all the soaring, devilish thoughts I allowed in my head. I gave myself up unto the Devil and contracted with him for a term of twenty-four years, setting my body and soul in forfeit. Now are these twenty-four years run out. I have only this night left. An hourglass standeth before mine eyes, and I watch for it to finish.

I know that the Devil will have his due. As I have consigned my body and soul unto him with my blood in return for certain other costly considerations, I have no doubt that he will this night fetch me. This is why, dear and well-beloved, gracious Lords, I have summoned you here just before the end to take one last cup with me, not concealing from you the manner of my departure. I entreat you now, my dear gracious Brothers and Lords, to bring my cordial and brotherly greetings to my friends and to those who do honor my memory, to bear no ill will toward me but, if ever I have offended you, to forgive me in your hearts. As regardeth my *Historia* and what I have wrought in those twenty-four years, all these things have been written down for you.

Now let this my hideous end be an example unto you so long as ye may live, and a remembrance to love God and to entreat Him to protect you from the guile and the deceit of the Devil, praying that the Dear Lord will not lead you into temptation. Cling ye unto Him, falling not away from Him as I damned godless mortal have done, despising and denying Baptism (Christ's own Sacrament), God, all the Heavenly Host and mankind — such a sweet God, who desireth not that one shall be lost. Shun bad company, which would lead you astray as it hath me, go earnestly and often to church, war and strive constantly against the Devil with a steadfast faith in Christ and always walking a godly path.

Finally, my last request is that ye go to bed and let nothing trouble you, but sleep on and take your rest even if a crashing and tumult be heard in this house. Be not afraid. No injury shall befall you. Arise not out of your beds. Should ye find my corpse, convey it unto the earth, for I die both as a bad and as a good Christian. Contrition is in my heart, and my mind doth constantly beg for Grace and for the salvation of my soul. O I know that the Devil will have this body — and welcome he is to it, would he but leave my soul in peace. Now I entreat you: betake yourselves to bed. A good night to you — unto me, an evil, wretched and a frightful one.

Faustus needed great resolve and courage to make this confession and to tell his tale without weakening and becoming fearful and faint. As for the students, they were cast into great wonderment that a man could be so reckless as thus to imperil body and soul for no more profit than knavery, knowledge and sorcery. But, as they loved him well, they sought to console him thus:

Alas dear Fauste, how have ye imperiled yourself! Why remained ye so long silent, revealing none of these things to us? Why, we should have brought learned *Theologi* who would have torn you out of the Devil's nets and saved you. But now it is too late and surely injurious to body and soul.

Doctor Faustus answered, saying: Such was not permitted me. Often was I amind to seek counsel and succor of godfearing men. Indeed, once an old man did charge me to follow his teachings, leave my sorcery and be converted. Then came the Devil, ready to put an end to me (even as he will this night do), saying that in the moment of my conversion — nay, even in the instant of such an intent on my part—all would be over with me.

Upon hearing these words, and understanding that the Devil would surely dispatch Faustus this night, the students urged him to call upon God, begging Him for forgiveness for Jesus Christ's sake, saying:

130

O God, be merciful unto me poor sinner, and enter not into judgement with me, for I cannot stand before Thee. Although I must forfeit my body unto the Devil, wilt Thou preserve my soul!

Faustus agreed to do this. He tried to pray, but he could not. As it was with Cain, who said his sins were greater than could be forgiven him, so was it with Faustus also, who was convinced that in making his written contract with the Devil he had gone too far. But the students and good lords prayed and wept for Faustus. They embraced one another and, leaving Faustus in his chambers, retired to bed, where none could rightly sleep, for they lay there awake, waiting the end.

And it came to pass between twelve and one o'clock in the night that a great blast of wind stormed against the house, blustering on all sides as if the inn and indeed the entire neighborhood would be torn down. The students fell into a great fear, got out of their beds and came together to comfort one another, but they did not stir out of their chamber. The innkeeper went running out of the house, however, and he found that there was no disturbance at all in any other place than his own. The students were lodged in a chamber close by those of Doctor Faustus, and over the raging of the wind they heard a hideous music, as if snakes, adders and other serpents were in the house. Doctor Faustus' door creaked open. There then arose a crying out of Murther! and Help! but the voice was weak and hollow, soon dying out entirely.

When it was day the students, who had not slept this entire night, went into the chamber where Doctor Faustus had lain, but they found no Faustus there. The parlor was full of blood. Brain clave unto the walls where the Fiend had dashed him from one to the other. Here lay his eyes, here a few teeth. O it was a hideous *spectaculum*. Then began the students to bewail and beweep him, seeking him in many places. When they came out to the dung heap, here they found his corpse. It was monstrous to behold, for head and limbs were still twitching.

131

These students and magisters who were present at Faustus' death gained permission afterwards to bury him in the village. Subsequently, they retired to his domicile where they found the famulus Wagner already mourning his master. This little book,

It was monstrous to behold

Doctor Faustus His Historia, was already all written out. Now as to what his famulus wrote, that will be a different, new book. On this same day the enchanted Helen and her son Justus Faustus were also gone.

So uncanny did it become in Faustus' house that none could dwell there. Doctor Faustus himself walked about at night, making revelations unto Wagner as regardeth many secret matters. Passers-by reported seeing his face peering out at the windows.

Now this is the end of his quite veritable deeds, tale, *Historia* and sorcery. From it the students and clerks in particular should learn to fear God, to flee sorcery, conjuration of spirits, and other works of the Devil, not to invite the Devil into their houses, nor to yield unto him in any other way, as Doctor Faustus did, for we have before us here the frightful and horrible example of his pact and death to help us shun such acts and pray to God alone in all matters, love Him with all our heart and with all our soul and with all our strength, defying the Devil with all his following, that we may through Christ be eternally blessed. These things we ask in the name of Christ Jesus our only Lord and Savior. Amen. Amen.

BIBLIOGRAPHICAL NOTE

It is difficult to draw from the large quantity of Faust commentary of the past hundred years a selection which can be recommended to the general reader as neither recondite detailwork directed solely at scholars nor, on the other hand, shallow, generally erroneous popularization. Only on the broad subject of the Faust theme can excellent books be found in various languages:

Geneviève Bianquis, *Faust à travers quatre siècles* (Paris, 1935).

Karl Theens, *Doctor Johann Faust: Geschichte der Faustgestalt* (Meisenheim, 1948).

Eliza Marian Butler, *Faust Through the Ages* (Cambridge, England, 1952).

Charles Dédéyan, *Le thème de Faust dans la littérature européene,* 4 vols. (Paris, 1954).

Related to the above works, in that they reproduce texts of many fictional treatments of the Faust theme, are Karl G. Wendriner's collection, *Die Faustdichtung vor, neben und nach Goethe* (Berlin, 1913), and *Gestaltungen des Faust,* 3 vols. (Munich, 1927), edited by the novelist Horst W. Geissler. Here should also be mentioned two works which contain many pictorial representations of Faust and his deeds: Franz Neubert, *Vom Doctor Faustus zu Goethes Faust* (Leipzig, 1932), and Wolfgang Wegner, *Die Faustdarstellung vom 16. Jahrhundert bis zur Gegenwart* (Amsterdam, 1962).

Oskar Schade, *Faust vom Ursprung bis zur Verklärung durch*

135

Goethe (Berlin, 1912), and Vincenzo Errante, *Il mito di Fausto del personaggio storico al poema di Goethe* (Bologna, 1924), are, as the titles indicate, restricted to the period from the sixteenth through the eighteenth centuries. Philip M. Palmer and Robert P. More, *The Sources of the Faust Tradition* (New York, 1936), is a collection of important source texts on forerunners of Faust as well as on Faust before Goethe. Here the reader can find, for example, the Theophilus novel in translation from the Greek, or the records of the historical Faust referred to in my introduction. Palmer and More also offers the most convenient reprinting of the 1592 English Faust Book, unless one prefers the modernized version by William Rose, *History of the Damnable Life and Deserved Death of Doctor John Faustus* (London, 1930).

A facsimile edition of the 1587 Spiess Faust Book was published by Wilhelm Scherer as *Das älteste Faust-Buch* (Berlin, 1884). The long-standard critical edition was that by Robert Petsch, *Das Volksbuch vom Doktor Faust* (Halle, 1921). A more recent one is by Hans Henning, *Historia Von D. Johann Fausten* (Halle, 1963). A diplomatic edition of the Wolfenbüttel Manuscript is available in H. G. Haile's *Das Faustbuch* (Berlin, 1963). All these editions contain introductions and appendices which evaluate Faust-Book research, but it should be pointed out that Hans Henning is not acquainted with recent work on the history of the text.

Both Petsch and Henning devote a section of their introductions to the historical Faust. The treatment in my introduction to the present book is based largely on the findings of Hans Henning. There will probably always be those who are fascinated by the historical figure to the exclusion of the literary one, but since our factual records are scanty, such books tend to consist largely of conjecture. Karl Kiesewetter, *Faust in Geschichte und Tradition* (Leipzig, 1893), probes into the parapsychological powers of Faust, and Henri Birven, *Der historische Doktor Faust: Maske und Antlitz* (Gelnhausen, 1963), seeks to show that Faust was a serious but popularly maligned scholar.